Shiatsu & The Art of Conscious Cooking

Written & Published by Joanne Faulkner

It is intended that recipes and recommendations within this book complement, not substitute professional medical guidance and medication. The author or publisher is not responsible for any adverse effects resulting from the use of suggestions in this book. Readers are encouraged to seek their own body's wisdom and experience for guidance.

Published by Joanne Faulkner
www.joannefaulkner.org

Book Design and Photography by Kate Hynes
www.behance.net/katemaria
Illustrations and Artwork by Joanne Faulkner
Additional photography Emma Brereton and Joanne Faulkner
Back cover design and promotional material Therese Wright
Web app design Victor Terentiev - www.dulingame.com

Printed on recycled paper

A catalogue record for this book is available from the British library.

STAINLESS STEEL
中国制造
MADE IN CHINA

Contents:

Introduction

All different — All the same

The word "Shiatsu" comes from "Shi"(finger) and "Atsu" (pressure) which involves comfortable pressure applied to the "acupuncture" points and energy channels in the body. This system of complementary medicine is said to be over four thousand years old. In Shiatsu and Traditional Chinese Medicine, food and drink are used for dietary healing and support. The body is classified into yin/yang organ pairs and meridians (pathways), these correspond to emotions, flavours, seasons and colours. So when treating the body through acupressure and manipulation of meridians, using the table below as guiding principles, I recommend specific foods that further support the body and bring it back to balance.

flavour	season	meridians & organs	properties	emotion	colour
pungent	autumn	lung/large intestine	consolidation & boundaries	grief /letting go	white
salty	winter	kidney/ bladder	core foundation of calm & being	fear	blue /black
sour	spring	liver/gall bladder	dynamic, flexible & effective	anger /creativity	green
bitter	high summer	heart/small intestine	expansion	joy	red
sweet	late summer	spleen/ stomach	centering & supporting	satisfaction /mothering	orange

It's a very easy system to follow and I have translated this ancient practice into an easy to follow, modern cook book containing recipes, meditations and acupressure points, explaining the links between food, emotions and the physical body. When we look at ourselves in this holistic way we can achieve a state of health, balance and well being.

An easy example is a person who is craving chocolate; they are looking for sweet foods that relate to the Late Summer and the Stomach/Spleen, so I would recommend sweet roasted vegetables that connect to that harvest time of year and millet which is an alkalizing grain perfect for bringing a sensation of satisfaction to the Spleen.

Someone who is feeling hot headed and frustrated I would associate with the Liver/Gallbladder so I would recommend plenty of raw greens such as flat leaf parsley and spinach to increase detox and flow within the body.

A person who is very pale and suffers with constant coughs and colds would need their immune system strengthening and therefore I would recommend pungent foods such as ginger and garlic to fortify the Lung/Large Intestine.

A carrot is a carrot is a carrot yet we all digest carrots differently. Once it enters our bodies it becomes more than calorific content and a collection of vitamins and minerals. It is transformed into our unique life force.

As babies we all began our life with milk, whether breast or formula, yet even if you gave ten babes exactly the same milk at exactly the same time/temperature/place, they would all grow and change at different rates. Some would be podgy, some would grow tall, some would have colic and some would have none. Therefore food is not just about what we eat, it is about our genetic inheritance, our mental state, our culture, our physical atmosphere and much more besides. Therefore food itself is only part of a balanced diet. It is our connection to food and drink which is just as important as it mirrors our connection to life. Do we see food as a scary enemy, does it frighten us? Do we have fierce control over it, governing what and when we eat with no space for joy? Do we eat on the run using food as simple fuel with no time to taste the dishes and smell the coffee? Do we feel at home in our bodies, responding to its physical appetite with love, affection, vitality and juicy excitement? Can we receive the great abundance life has for us or does guilt and shame limit our intake? Our ability to receive has just as much impact as the type or amount of food we eat. Ability to receive can be termed another way do we let love in.

Love is the Yin to the Yang of Eating and Drinking, for healthy life balance you can't have one without the other.

How to Use This Book

This book is not aimed at being prescriptive. You can come with a presenting problem and look up the answer – which food will I cook? Which points will I press? But it cannot change or cure you, only you have that authority. This book aims to bring you into deep balanced connection with your body and soul so that you can find a solution to support or restore you, whether that is diet, counselling or chemotherapy. Life is a journey and I find awareness and responsibility for ones own path makes the adventure more magical and often less painful. So with a clear and uncluttered mind ask three questions and listen as your body gives the answer.

1. How am I feeling right now?
2. What do I need right now?
3. How can I love myself more?

You are not allowed to say "I don't know" to any of the above questions. Somewhere, in some part of your body you do know. It may be tricky to access; it does take practice and patience. Sometimes you may get an image or a memory. Sometimes a bodily sensation like pins and needles or heat or cold in some part of your internal/external body, perhaps a taste on your tongue. You may hear words or a

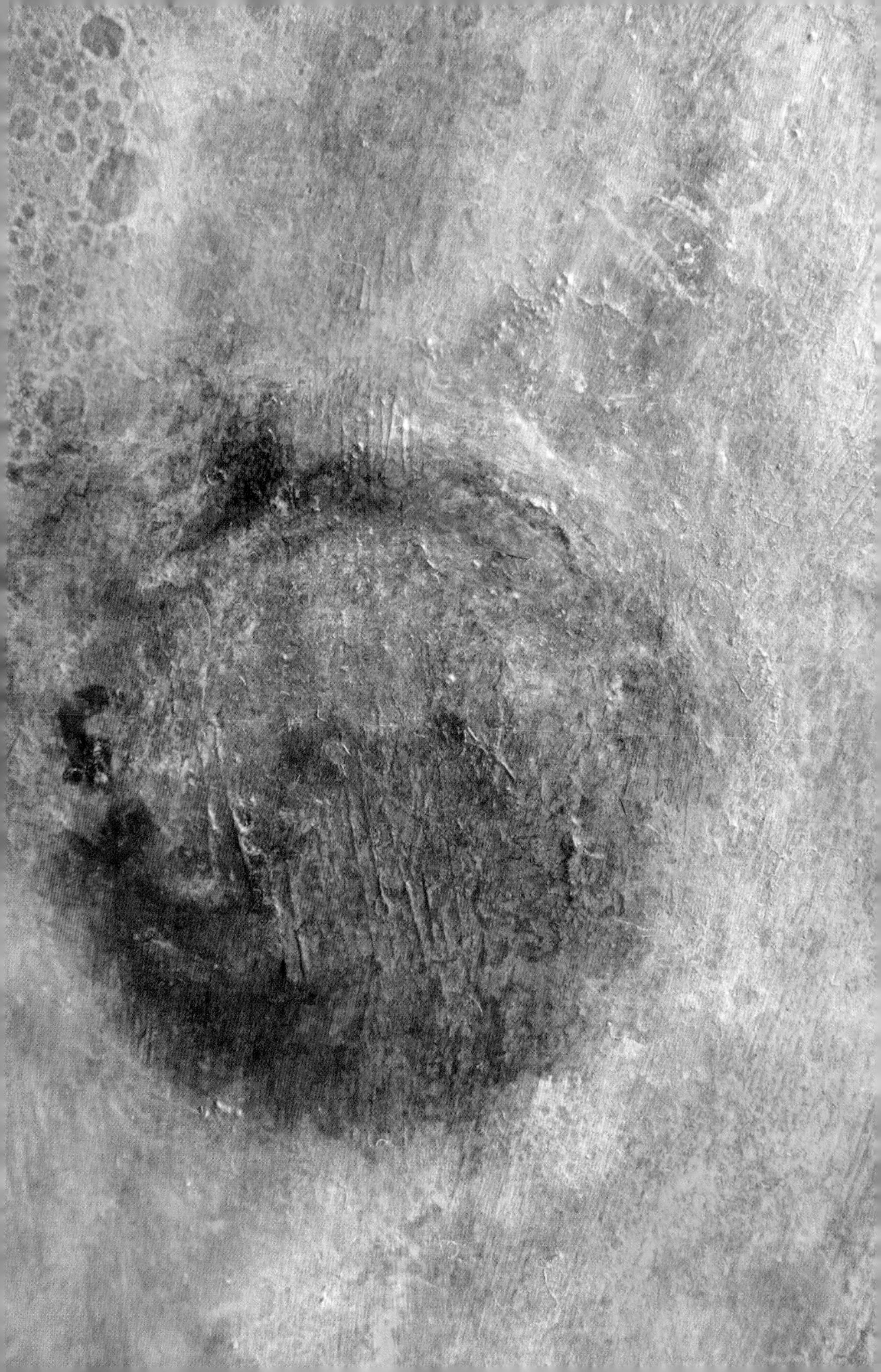

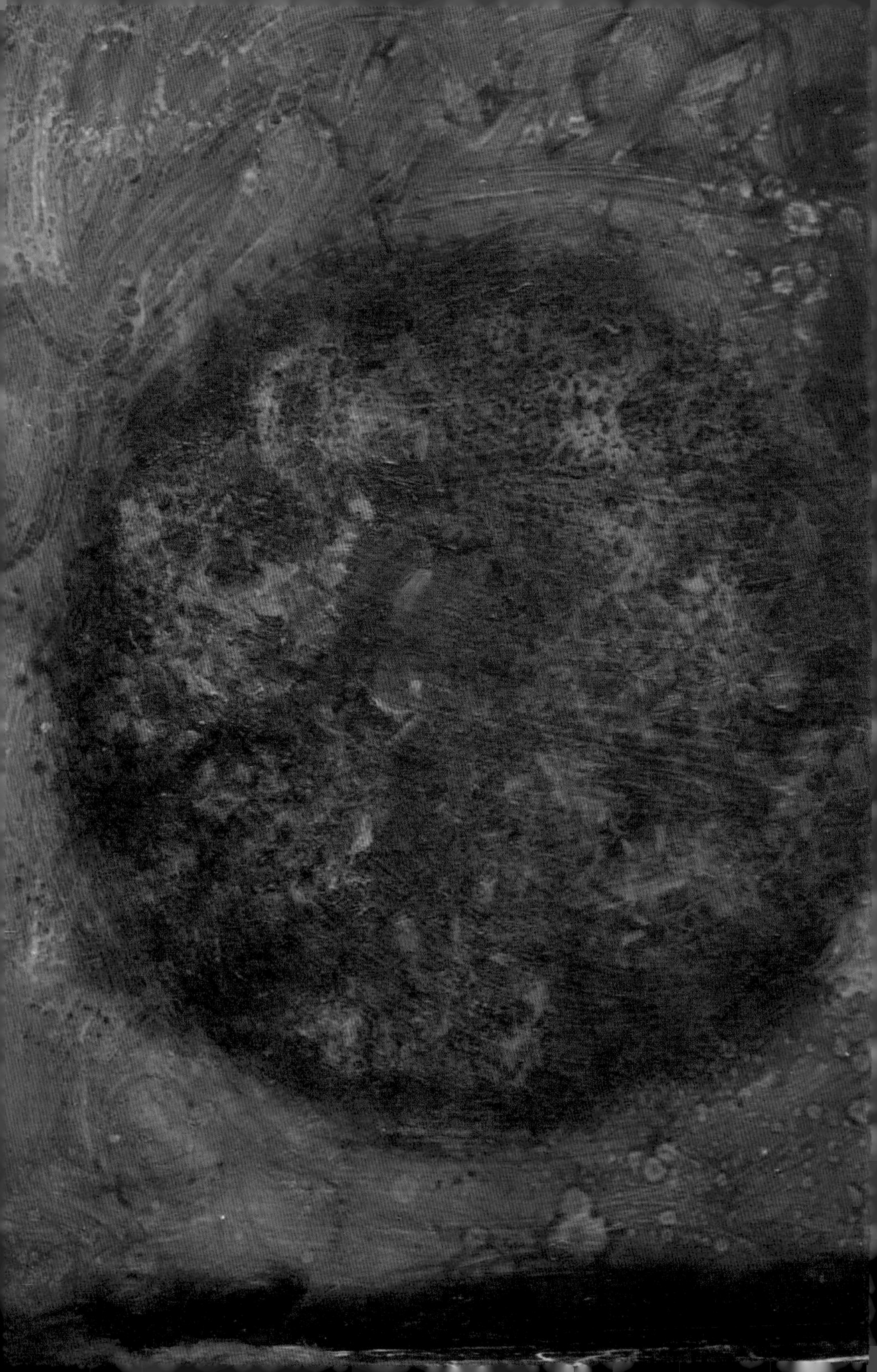

lyric of a song. All these are messages from your body, don't ignore them. Listen to your mind/body with compassion and look after yourself as you would your own child.

"Prayer is the language we use to speak to God — Silence is the language God uses to speak to us"
Eckhart Tolle

Acceptance

When we ask "How am I feeling?" It is possible that uncomfortable feelings arise – maybe we are angry – in fact furious but we don't want to feel angry, we want to feel peace and love and that everything is alright with the world. Unfortunately that would not be the truth of how we are in this moment. To be truly connected to ourselves we must be honest. It is really the only way to change the situation and to love ourselves because that requires acceptance. We have to accept who we are, how we feel and what we want.

To support ourselves in being honest we must accept our answers unreservedly. Acceptance doesn't mean we have to act upon our feelings or desires but we acknowledge that's how we feel in the moment. This book has many recipes that include sugar, chocolate, butter and other such items that are seen as extremely desirable but "bad" for us. I don't like to demonise food and make it the problem. Rather to go inside and truthfully ask three questions and with honesty, take responsibility for our feelings, meeting our desires and loving ourselves more.

Obviously you may have desires for foods that are not going to be "good" for you. But really there are no good and bad foods, there are only foods that will and will not meet our true needs. Craving chocolate is a prime example. In my clinic I hear lots of people who if they could have anything they wanted with no consequences they would gorge on chocolate. To me this points to an underlying lack of support in a person's life, they are mentally exhausted and need some tender loving care. Whilst there is nothing wrong with chocolate it cannot love you, it cannot hug you, it cannot stop the worrying thoughts that go around and around in your head. So be honest, is having that extra slice of cake or chocolate biscuit really loving yourself more? When meeting needs with food and drink, it is possible to get caught in an addictive cycle. Bringing the third question about love into our consciousness will hopefully bring great honesty and awareness enabling us to truly meet our needs and love ourselves more. We are all on a journey towards this physical body decaying and dying, surely the journey is about how we can enjoy that body, take care of it and nurture it like the precious object that it is.

Tuning In

To strive for perfection is exhausting and futile. As we will see in the yin/yang chapter to have perfection without imperfection would be impossible. The point is not to work at getting it right but just to breathe and have a go. No two moments are the same, we are ever changing in each moment, so don't aim to be perfect but to be present, to be conscious and connected. To see how the body is, how the mind is and what does it need right now for balance and harmony. It is a constant circle of consciousness and awareness. As we become more connected and aware of ourselves, we become awake to more possibilities and solutions, which means we are more aware and so on and so on, ever expanding, ever deepening our engagement and understanding of life.

What we are today comes from our thoughts of yesterday and present thoughts build our life of tomorrow: our life is the creation of our mind. ***The Buddha***

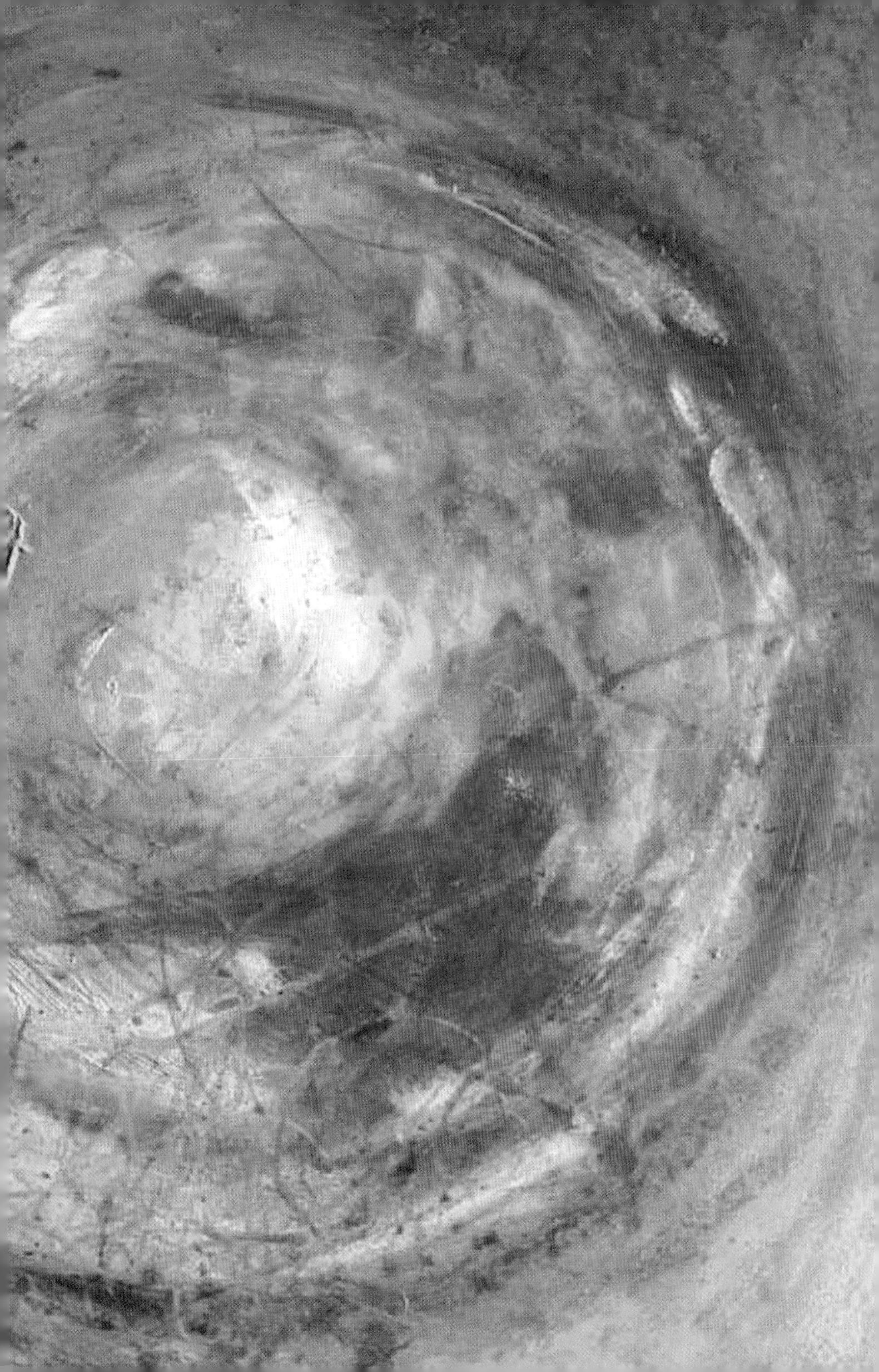

More about Feeling — Mind Body/Body Mind

In many eastern traditions there is an acceptance that the body and mind are integrated and inseparable. Whereas in the west we tend to think of the mind as the brain and in control, that the body is merely a vehicle for the mind. It gets us from A to B and carries out the functions we ask, such as making cups of tea, cooking lasagne, cycling the kids to school etc. Sometimes I give it optimum fuel and at other times I ignore problems and drive myself until I break. My body is used to do my bidding, but whose bidding? Me, my thinking mind, my personality, my ego. Most of the time unfortunately my thinking mind is in charge. Operating in the present, using judgements from the past and guesses about the future. The mind, operating as ego, likes to think that it's in control and doing all the decision making, but really it's not the best driver. I like to see my body as super intelligent and when used together with the thinking mind, I can use them to access true wisdom. Think back and remember a time when you walked into a room and even though nothing was being said you could sense an atmosphere. Perhaps there had been an argument before you walked in or a secret declaration of love. The body knows. It tells the mind which then tells the body the appropriate action, all in a split second. So much so we cannot separate them and within this book if the mind or body are mentioned, understand that the meaning is of the inseparable mind/body or body/mind. Hormones are another great example of this intertwining body/mind. For women, hormones change within a monthly cycle which can affect thoughts and feelings and for men, changes in testosterone also lead to mood swings and changes in behaviour. This is the body affecting the mind, conversely if we are worried about something and it is constantly playing on our mind this will affect our stomach and spleen. Ringing true the phrase, "knots in our stomach". Our thoughts can manifest physically in our bodies and our physical condition influences our mental state. The body gives us information all the time as to how we are and what we need, the trouble is that the mind, is often over thinking, constantly trying to stay in control and protect itself. If we open our minds to the possibility that our body might have an opinion and if we give it space to speak, it is possible to live with a greater understanding of ourselves, our actions and the world we create; being in our bodies in this way means living our life in love.

For help and guidance in using this book I have asked myself the three questions on different days and here are a few examples;

A rainy day in November, Bray Dart Station.

How am I feeling? Today I would say am feeling a bit sad with an underlying level of exhaustion. **What do I need right now?** To be held until I fell asleep and to sleep for at least ten hours. Unfortunately as a single mum with three kids under the age of seven that is unlikely to happen. **How can I love myself more?** However in my answer I can see I need human contact, relaxation and more sleep. So I could meet my need with a massage and an early night. But what am I actually doing? I am drinking coffee waiting for a train following an afternoon's shopping. This is not fulfilling the third question.

Cold Sunday Evening In November

How am I feeling? Exhausted, mentally more than anything. I feel I've been saying to the kids "don't do that" and "stop doing that" all day. We've been into town, out to the beach and had lovely friends drop in, unexpectedly, for dinner. Now the kids have been put to bed and there is just the decimation of the day to clear up. **What do I need right now?** I need a couple of glasses of port and abit of facebook interaction. **How can I love myself more?** Well y'know what I'm going to take those two things as loving myself in this moment. If I were to use drink or

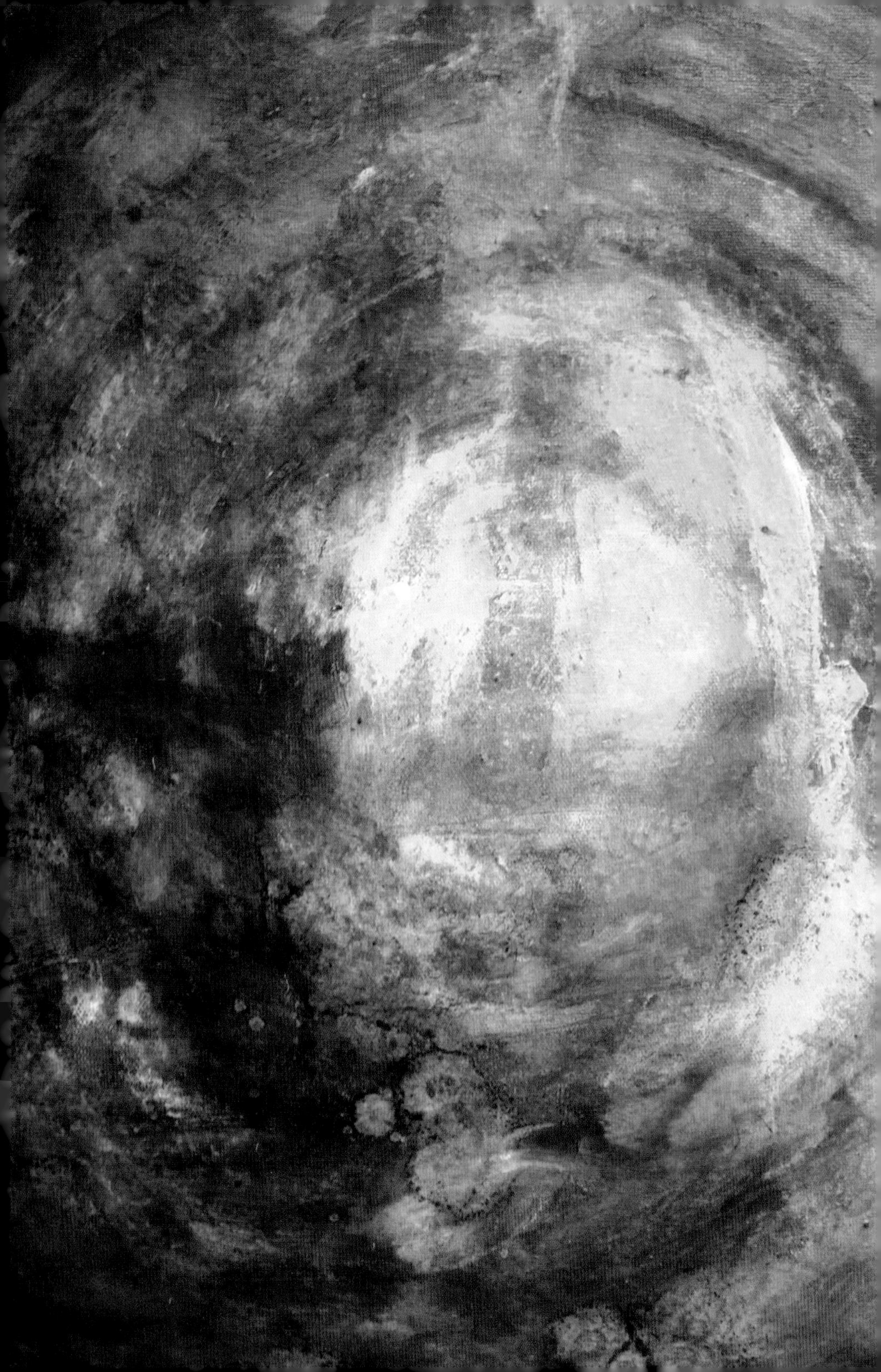

the internet constantly as a way to love myself that would not be healthy but just for tonight its ok. The asking and listening was me loving myself. Important to remember food and drink in itself will never solve a problem alone rather it is the connection to oneself that is the answer. As the great sage, my grandmother, said "a little of what you fancy does you good".

Very rainy Monday Morning

How am I feeling? A bit little girl lost. I feel like I keep wanting to check my facebook and see if anybody has contacted me. I feel I want to reach out to get the attention/ affection of others. **What do I need right now?** I I need to parent and give that little girl some attention so I'm going to paint and then I'm going to further use my creativity by trying out a new soup I have in mind. I feel like having a clear broth but sweet and spicy. The kids wont eat this so I'll make them tomato sauce with sweet potato and noodles (Aarons gums are slightly bloody so he needs some extra vitamin C from the sweet potato and tomato). **How can I love myself more?** By making this special dish for me I feel like I'm giving that little girl in me some extra attention, I'm going to have fun doing it too, be light today and not take anything too seriously, really follow my fun.

To be guided through the three questions to a recipe that suits you visit the free app shiatsu-consciouscooking.com/app

"If we could change ourselves, the tendencies in the world would also change. As a man changes his own nature, so does the attitude of the world change towards him... Be the change you wish to see in the world" **Mahatma Ghandi**

Chapter 1: Yin & Yang

Yin and yang represent the dynamic ebb and flow of life. Newton's third law states "for every action, there is an equal and opposite reaction". However Yin & Yang is not just about opposing forces but seeing movement and change as an interconnected whole.

It is not possible to attain a perfect state health, your body's always changing. Things that often seem real and solid are transforming imperceptibly before our very eyes. By understanding yin & yang, life becomes a journey full of interconnected shifts in balance rather than pursuits of goals and destinations.

Overview

In the west we are all familiar with veins and arteries that carry blood around the body. In Chinese Medicine there is a similar system which carries energy (chi) around the body. These energetic pathways are called Meridians. Meridians are usually understood in pairs:

yin	yang
lung	**large intestine**
kidney	**bladder**
liver	**gall bladder**
heart	**small intestine**
spleen	**stomach**
heart protector	**triple healer**

These pairs mirror the root concept of Traditional Chinese Medicine which is the principle of Yin and Yang. It's a common symbol, half black, half white each containing a dot of the others colour. This symbol represents the constant flux of the universe. The ultimate stillness of yin will produce movement of yang and after ultimate movement there will again be stillness.

The universe is constantly seeking balance; we see it in nature all the time. A surge in the rabbit population means predator population will also increase due to the availability of prey. These extra predators will cull the rabbit population which will eventually lead to a decline in their own predator population and so round and around the Yin/Yang spins, always changing, always seeking balance. A good example in our own bodies would be the common cold. Sometimes we take a chill and with this the body creates fever to heat the body up. If internal heat becomes too extreme we sweat to cool the body down again.

Yin and Yang are not separate, static entities rather the constant rolling relationship of energies, each one flows into the other creating the whole circle.

Our bodies and the food we eat is simply energy formed as matter and therefore in constant change. In some ways it is not possible to categorize foods as only yin or yang or apply them to only one element. Seaweeds are a good example. They strengthen the bodies' yin, helping it to regulate minerals and water levels; this assists in regulating our energy therefore boosting yang. Just like Yin Yang symbol, nothing is ever completely black and white.

yin	yang
water	**fire**
stability	**change**
inwards & downwards	**upwards & outwards**
quiet, dark & cool	**active, light & warm**
earth & vegetation	**sky & air**
nutrition, maintenance & storage	**mobilization for action**
seeing	**looking**
being	**doing**

To Nourish Yin

When the Yin is abundant there is an ability to receive and restore. The body and mind is fertile and receptive. We can liken the quality to the female womb, dark and still, waiting in the void for the moment to creative life. It is the still point from where Yang action arises. When deficient physically there is a tendency to heat and dryness, emotionally there is an inability to calm and soothe the system.

- Meditation and bodywork
- Sleep
- Regular relaxation
- Cultivate receptivity and allowing
- Yin is all about fluids therefore take care not to loose to much through sweating, purging therapies, childbirth, sex, overdoing spicy food, central heating, air conditioning
- Foods linked to the bodily fluids would be those that are especially mineral and vitamin rich (esp. salty and sour). Therefore seaweeds, wheatgrass, fish, wide range of vegetables pulses, grains and a little meat so that we get a full range of all the vitamins, minerals and trace elements
- Cook the foods with/in water for a short time
- Fruits also moisten and enhance fluids

To Nourish Yang

When Yang is abundant there is a warmth and vitality; a healthy will and engagement with life. One does not feel constrained or repressed. However when Yang is deficient there is a tendency to stagnation and dampness. Often there is a reliance on stimulants to create activity. This mimics the yang energy but in reality further depletes the system on a long term basis.

- Take exercise, ensuring you keep warm and incorporate body brushing
- Choose warming and pungent foods to counteract cold such as cinnamon, fennel, and horseradish
- Avoid raw and fatty foods which will further cool and create dampness respectively
- Cook foods for a longer time creating sweetness
- Fears can often cause the body to contract further creating cold and inertia. So find the inner warrior, face your fears (you don't have to do it anyway) but become inspired to follow your passion

Traditional Chinese Medicine is over 5000 years old and at times can be extremely complex but I believe that a journey with three questions from the Introduction (How do I feel? What do I need? How can I love myself more?) and a basic understanding of Yin/ Yang balance, it's a great way to connect with our own inner wisdom and take responsibility in caring for our own health and well being.

Q. How Am I Feeling?

yin	yang
cold	**warm / hot**
relaxed & centred	**active & expansive**
fluid / damp	**dry**
stable	**changeable**

Q. What do I need right now?

A. I feel my mind is overactive I need to calm down.

Q. How can I love myself more?

A. Why can't we stop thinking? Is it lack of sleep, is it hormonal, am I worried about something, am I trying to change or control something? I could eat some porridge to calm my nerves, or I could make some Chamomile tea. Food alone sometimes cannot solve problems as food is only part of a balanced diet for life. Perhaps I need a relaxing lavender bath and an early night or maybe learning meditation techniques might help.
We need to see the body as a whole system to achieve balance and wellness. But the right food at the right time sends a signal to our bodies that we love and care for ourselves which is fundamental to well being.

Yin & Yang Meditation

Set a candle in front of you either on the floor or on a table. First look at this candle watch it flicker, see the different parts of the flame, how the colours change and the movement in the air around it. See the surface it sits on, note the colour and texture. Do this for a couple of minutes then stop, take a drink or a few deep breaths and sit down again in front of the candle. This time relax the eyes. Instead of looking, try absorbing and receiving the whole image. You already know what it looks like so now just see it. As you relax your eyes they become less active and pointed in their looking. They perceive peripherally from a soft internal viewpoint. Turn the mind off, there's no need to think and assess the candle any more. It just is and you are taking two minutes to just see it.

This essentially represents the fundamental difference in energy between Yin and Yang. The yang assess the situation, it makes judgements and takes action upon them. Whereas the Yin doesn't need to change anything it accepts its place in the interconnectedness of everything and is anchored in the fundamental stream of life. One flows into the other in a beautiful ceaseless circle.

"Hate is not conquered by hate: Hate is conquered by love. This is a law eternal." ***The Buddha***

Tea Recipes for Yin & Yang

Let us begin with tea. There's something about tea and I don't just mean the black sort with milk and sugar but any preparation of hot drink that is cradled in the hands, brought to the mouth, breathed upon and taken in, warm and wet, that has about it a communion with community. It has a ritual element that is integral to culture, whether that be Japanese high tea ceremony or an Indian chai stall serving the three foot frothy pour. It is a drink in which we share a connection with our community of humanity. Something to bear in mind when you are preparing your brew, feel the connection to yourself and with your wider community. Know that there is support in the liquid and from the others who drink with you. All around the globe at this very instant many souls are taking a moment and savouring a *cuppa*.

	lung	kidney	liver	heart	spleen
cooling	cardamom chai	cranberry	dandelion coffee nettle	rosehip hawthorn valerian	cabbage & apple juice
warming	ginger chai	honey & warm apple cider vinegar	lemongrass	dandelion root	cinnamon
calming	warm almond milk	barley water	chrysan-themum	chamomile	vervian
energizing	black pepper & orange peel	kudzu	hot lemon juice	sage	fennel seed
neutral	carrageen moss	flaxseed	liquorice	green tea	basil, mint & caraway seed

Most of the above teas can be bought ready prepared but if you wish to prepare your own infusions use approximately 1 large teaspoon of the dried herb or 2 teaspoons of the fresh herb with 1 cup of hot water. Place the herbs in a teapot or cafetiere and

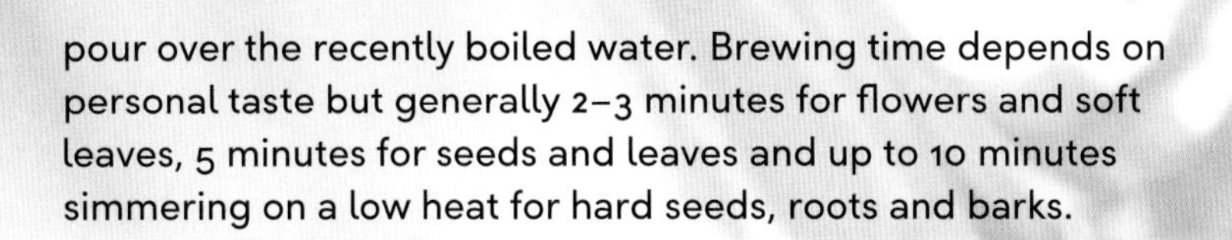

pour over the recently boiled water. Brewing time depends on personal taste but generally 2–3 minutes for flowers and soft leaves, 5 minutes for seeds and leaves and up to 10 minutes simmering on a low heat for hard seeds, roots and barks.

Cinnamon Tea

If you feel constantly wanting, always needy and crave some satisfaction.

Cinnamon creates heat within the body, increases the metabolism and at the same time lowers blood sugar and increases insulin. This is exactly what the stomach needs when we have been thinking too much, worrying too much and when we have set up a pattern of craving and desire. This tea will help our thinking mind to strengthen, settle and come home to ourselves with sweet satisfaction. Bring a pan with 500ml water and 1–2 cinnamon stick to the boil, simmer with a lid for 20 minutes then strain into your teapot. You may want to add roibosh tea, milk and a little honey, alternatively pour into a jug allow to cool and pour over ice as a sweet summer cooler.

Almond Milk

If you need to cool an inflamed chest or burning intestine

Blend 6 tablespoons of almonds with 1 pint of water until smooth and honey for flavour and strain through a fine sieve. This can be stored in a refrigerator for five to six days although it should be drunk daily to work at alleviating digestive, urinary and respiratory disorders.

Masala Chai

If you are feeling scattered and need a taste of comfort

1 tbls cinnamon bark
1 tbls cardamom pods
½ tables fresh ginger
1 star anise
5 cloves
2 pints water
Black tea and Milk optional

Often in India this tea will be made in the summer with Cardamom to have a cooling effect and with Ginger in the winter to heat the body. Every region and every household has their own recipe so experiment and see what you have in the cupboard. Bring to the boil all the ingredients in a large pan with approximately 1 ½ litres of water. Simmer for at least 10 minutes with the lid on and then add the black tea. Traditionally this is made with condensed milk in India but that may be a little too sweet to the taste and you may prefer to add a drop of milk and a teaspoon of honey.

Warming Flow

If you need to cool your kidneys

This will encourage a restful sleep and help treat urinary infections which can heat the body. Warm a small glass of Apple Cider Vinegar, add a little honey and drink half an hour before bed. This can also improve digestive disorders and improves liver function.

Stomach Calming

If you are overly active and in need of calm

1 tsp basil
1 tsp mint
1 tsp fennel or caraway seeds

Simply pour boiling water over ingredients and allow to brew for

5 minutes. The mint will cool the stomach and the basil will calm the heart. The fennel and caraway seeds are antispasmodic and can soothe the muscles in the digestive process easing colic and the accumulations of gas and fluids.

Ginger Tea

If you feel shivery and cold and need some warming up

Fresh Ginger
Honey (optional)
Thyme (optional)

Roughly chop or finely grate an inch of fresh ginger, pour on boiling water add the optional ingredients and let it brew for a few minutes. Ginger is very warming to the system, increasing the circulation in the whole body; Great at cutting through phlegm and clearing infection.

Cranberry Juice

If you feel hot in the lower burner

Many people already know that cranberries can reduce the acidity of urine, treat cystitis and other urinary tract infections. They can stop harmful bacteria attaching to the bladder walls and can prevent kidney stones. However many commercially produced juices contain high amounts of sugar which heat the system and counteract the benefits of the berry. So to make your own heat 50g of fresh cranberries with 100ml of water, simmer for about 10 minutes until the skins pop. Blend the mixture and strain through a fine sieve and add more warm water, honey or lemon to taste.

Hot Lemon Water

If you feel sluggish and in need of some spring in your step

The simplest way to get your liver working and therefore put a spring in your step is to drink the juice of half a lemon in hot water first thing in the morning. Taken at night it can reduce cramps and restless legs syndrome. For a lemon drink boil 3 sliced lemons in 1 litre of water until the liquid is reduced by half, add honey to taste. Lemons are packed full of vitamin C and have an alkalizing effect on the whole system.

Chapter 2: Lung & Large Intestine

flavour	pungent
season	autumn
meridians & organs	lung & large intestine
properties	consolidation & boundaries
emotion	grief/ letting go
colour	white

Overview

Summer is over, everything is harvested and with the Autumn we turn inwards, preparing for the stillness of the winter. The transition of seasons shows us that everything changes. Summer comes, everything flourishes, in winter it dies back only to be reborn again through spring. It's the cycle of life. We are born and our life is a rollercoaster journey toward death. In whatever way you choose to believe, after death our body will transform. Whether that is into nutrients in the soil, as an angel or as incarnation of the exact karmic opposite of this life. We will change and transform. Autumn, connected to the Lung and Large Intestine is the important time of transition and transformation, taking stock of who we are and how we operate in the world.

Every day cells in our body die and they are replaced by new cells. As we age, the rate of replacement and regeneration slows. Nonetheless old cells are broken down within the body and eliminated. We let go of our dead cells. Our body has to, if we hold onto them it can create blockages, pain and disease. This is the internal process and it is the same for the external. Things and people come into our life and as a natural process, they leave us. The letting go can be painful and our emotion to express this pain is grief. Grief is the emotion of the Lung & Large Intestine. It is an essential emotion, it shows we have a connection to the world around us and it means that our compassion is active. By connecting to the sadness and grief created by the comings and goings of life we connect with our own mortality and the reality of life. Failure to let go of things or people or inability to connect with reality and sometimes sadness, will affect the Lung and Large

Intestine. Remember a time when you really cried. It can be hard to catch your breath almost as if breath causes the pain to be felt more deeply but as the sobs subside the chest softens and we breathe smoothly again coming to terms with what is, with an acceptance and vulnerability.

The lung is how we connect at every second to the world and life around us. We breathe. We smell. We feel the atmosphere. We take in the air and use its ingredients to give us life.

We can live for a long time without food and some yogis take their water by breathing the dew in the air. But without breath we only survive a matter of minutes. It is our connection to the cycle of life. So no matter how deep our wound and our pain, we cannot let our breathing become impaired, we must carry on connecting and participating in life, understanding that all things shall pass.

The skin is often named as the third lung in Chinese Medicine so complaints which surface here such as psoriasis and eczema, often have their roots in the Lung/Large Intestine realm. Irritable Bowel Syndrome is also on the increase. To nourish and strengthen the Lung & Large Intestine, in all its realms, there are a range of great foods to take and to avoid, but most importantly we must breathe properly. Breathe right down into our large intestine, connect the two so that oxygen penetrates all of our body and it operates as a whole connected system. To make sure you are doing this put one hand on your upper chest and the other on your stomach, breathe normally – which hand moves? Ideally it should be the lower hand operating, meaning your diaphragm is opening all of your lungs rather that the muscles of your upper chest shallowly operating the top half of your lungs. So now as you breathe right

and orange is surrounding and protecting you, like the Ready Brek Man, loving you and the skin you are in.
The Lung & Large Intestine are linked to the physical earthly body that ceases to exist when we die. The lungs take in the air, the large intestine eliminates the waste. When they are functioning at their peak they create a strong boundary. In our western medicine we label it 'immune system'. With every breath the lung is subject to all kinds of germs pathogens and virus's. If our immune system is operating they are expelled on the out breath and only what we need is absorbed. The same can be said for the Large Intestine, its wall needs to be strong so that debris waste and toxins are not reabsorbed into the body. Two organs doing their job, taking in and letting go, working within the constant push pull of connecting to the world whilst not being overwhelmed by it; retaining our sense of self whilst open to the reality and opportunities of life.

Foods at a glance for Lung & Large Intestine

Warming and Drying	Moistening and Cooling
Ginger — Dried and Fresh	**Yogurt**
Shitake Mushrooms	**Almonds**
Cardamom,	**Avocado**
Cinnamon, Cloves	**Banana**
Onions/Leeks/Garlic	**Carrageen Moss**

Lung Meditation

For this meditation I am going to use the Tibetan Buddhist practice of Tonglen. This practice is to transform negative emotions. It is not to deny them or push them away but rather not to attach to them and watch as they dissolve enabling you to breathe fully and expand into the whole hearted person you are.

Firstly sit and centre yourself. Try and ensure your back is as straight as possible and if you need to, shut your eyes. How are you feeling, in pain, grief or anger? If it helps, imagine that emotion as an object or a person, anything that fits the feeling into a form. Now swirl up the feeling or the object in a cloud of grey smoke and breathe it in, right in to your lungs and heart, feel it dissolve. As you breathe out, imagine white smoke, as clear and bright as light leaving your lungs from deep within. Do this over and over again. Breathing in the grey sticky cloud wrapped around your object, breathing out the clear white light. There is no need to analyse the emotion or wonder why it's there and what caused it. Just as we trust the large intestine to eliminate waste without it re entering our system. Allow the grief, anger, sadness or pain to pass through, enabling us to expand into new space and a clear mind.

It is said that King Solomon, feeling blue, asked his advisors to find him a ring he had seen in a dream. "When I feel satisfied I'm afraid that it won't last. And when I don't, I am afraid my sorrow will go on forever. Find me the ring that will ease my suffering." Eventually an advisor met an old jeweller who carved into a simple gold band the Hebrew inscription ***gamzeh ya'avor — this too shall pass.***

Onion and Miso Soup

I love onions, I love that sweetness they have when cooked slowly to a honey caramel colour. I know they can make you cry, I even love the tears they bring, like watching a weepy film, a good cry can often make you feel better. It strips away the stodgy feeling and leaves you feeling softly open, vulnerable and very huggable. That's what this soup does for me. It is my ultimate comfort soup; I feel very loved when I eat this soup, extra hugs come with a couple of buttered slices of spelt bread.

Any of the onion family are great for clearing phlegm from the chest. They have a pungency to them which is able to cut through damp congestion and fight infections. At the other end they are vital to maintain a balance of bacteria in the large intestine.

25 g butter
Good splash of toasted sesame oil
1.5 kg onions
Large sprig of fresh thyme
4 crushed Bay leaves
2 pints miso stock (to taste)

Melt the butter, add the onions and fry for a minute or so on a high heat. Give them a shuffle and a stir, making sure the butter doesn't burn and the onions don't stick. Throw in the herbs, bay leaves, splash of sesame oil and turn the heat down to the lowest possible setting, leaving the lid on. The onions need to cook for 20–30 minutes until they are a toffee colour and sticky consistency. Pour in the miso stock and simmer for at least another 20–30 minutes. The longer the better. A slow soup in the making but definitely worth the wait.

Spelt Bread

This recipe is here because I have seen an increase in skin disorders such as psoriasis and eczema. I believe this is due to the increase in refined products such as sugars and flours in our diet. There is less dietary fibre in these refined substances and so the intestine has to work extremely hard to move them. As the skin is the third lung problems in the large intestine will often show up as sensitivity on the skin. Check to see if your skin itches more or is slightly blotchy after eating something extremely sweet and refined like an iced bun or a couple of pieces of white bread toast. Spelt bread is great because the wheat berry has not been refined and the body finds it easy to digest. Another reason this recipe is here is because it's so simple. I once heard a man say "if you don't have time to bake a loaf of bread in your day, you don't have time for your life". I thought he was crazy but more and more I agree although I don't bake this loaf every day, I do make it about twice a week, once with the roast on a Sunday, ready for lunch boxes on Monday and once midweek. There is nothing to make you feel more like a competent cook and in control of your own kitchen than baking your own bread.

500g Organic Whole wheat Spelt Flour
1 tsp salt
1 tsp fast action yeast
14 fl oz warm water from recently boiled kettle
1 tbsp honey
1 tbsp olive oil

Measure out the flour into a large bowl, mixing in the salt and the yeast. In a jug measure out the water, which should be hot enough to put your finger in but not to leave it there. Then dissolve in the honey. Add the water to the bowl with flour and stir vigorously. When all the ingredients are mixed pour over

the olive oil and knead it in using your hands or a spoon. Tip the mixture into a buttered 2lb bread tin, bless it and leave it in a warm place to prove and rise for about an hour. Keep an eye on it, if your room is very hot it may prove quicker. When it has risen the height of the bread tin it is ready to go an oven at 180° for about 45 minutes. When it is cooked the underside should sound hollow like a drum. Make sure you turn it out onto a metal rack to cool, if you leave it in the tin condensation will form and the bread will be soggy. So easy you'll never buy bread again.

Shiitake Mushroom Risotto

All types of mushrooms help to decrease fat levels in the blood and boost immunity by increasing the white blood cell count. However oriental mushrooms such as shiitake contain interferon and beta glucans which help to increase immunity and reparation following cancer. They fall into this chapter because in Chinese medicine they also remove excess mucus from the lungs and promote smooth functioning intestines. For me that warm earthy flavour makes for perfect comfort food on an autumnal evening.

60g butter
60g olive oil
300g Arborio rice
1 Medium onion, diced
2-3 cloves of smashed garlic
5 large Shitake Mushrooms,
200 ml Dashi broth
1200 ml Vegetable stock
120g parsley, chopped
Juice of 1 lemon
60g Parmesan, grated
Salt and pepper to taste

The first thing to do is make the dashi broth by soaking the shitake mushrooms for 30 minutes in water from a recently boiled kettle. Meanwhile melt half the butter and the oil in a large heavy based saucepan. When the oil is hot add the onions and soften them on a medium heat for five minutes. Then add the garlic, finely sliced shitake mushrooms and half the parsley, softly frying for another five minutes before adding the rice, stir it for a few minutes so that all the grains are coated with buttery juices. Now add the Dashi broth, stirring constantly until it has been absorbed by the rice. The Dashi broth and the vegetable stock, must be kept at a gentle simmer so as not to interrupt the cooking of the rice when adding to the pot. Do the same with stock adding a ladle full (approx 100ml) at a time. After 15-20 minutes the stock should have been completely absorbed leaving a creamy sauce in which the soft rice sits. Stir in the remaining butter, parsley, parmesan and lemon juice to taste.

Hunky, chunky warming lentil stew

Every café worth its salt will be serving this recipe or variations at this time of year. The spices used here are warming to the system. Cardamom is a super spice for the Autumn. It can neutralize the mucus forming properties of dairy and aids digestion of fats and starches which can over cool the system and cause dampness. Cardamom warms and moisturises the bronchi and the digestive system. Its stimulating effect is holistic for the body as it is said to bring joy and good humour to the mind and everyone needs abit of that to feel good. However beware of eating the pods themselves as the taste if chewed is quite different than that of the flavour it gives. If you overload the chilli in this recipe you will see yin yang in action. The chilli's internal heating of the body will cause pores to open and sweat for form on the skin, so cooling the body and bringing it back to balance, which is fine if you have a cold and want to sweat it out. But this recipe is not about overdoing the chilli but about keeping the mucus membranes in the Lung & Large Intestine warm and moving. Ensuring we are surrounded by a warm protective glow that comes from the inside.

1 onion
3 cloves garlic
1 stick of celery
1 tsp fresh ginger
1 tsp cumin powder
1 tsp coriander powder
1½ tsp chilli
1 carrot
1 parsnip
¼ turnip
100g of red lentils
100g of green lentils
1½ pints of stock
3 cardamon pods
Cinnamon stick

Melt the oil and butter ensuring they are hot before adding the onions. Fry the onions for a couple of minutes, stirring frequently. Turn down the heat and add the celery. Sauté these on a medium heat for 5 minutes until they are translucent and soft. Add the ginger, garlic and dry spices, frying and stirring for about three minutes. At this point there should be a definite aroma which is making your nose tingle. Add the carrot, parsnip, turnip, red and green lentils. Turn the heat down low and let all the ingredients sweat for a few minutes. Don't let them stick or/and burn. Pour in the stock, stirring in the cardamom pods and cinnamon; allow it to come to a boil before putting on the lid and simmering for half an hour. I usually season with salt and pepper at the very end ensuring the beans or lentils don't become tough. This is great over rice or the same as the soup with a thick slice of buttered spelt.

Home Made Cough Syrup

Onions are surrounded by many old wives tales in their medicinal purposes. For example they are said to draw harmful bacteria to them so if you have flu or such like within the house leave a cut half of onion in the bedroom over night. This is said to draw out and capture the virus and harmful bacteria. In the morning throw the onion away. The same is said for the fridge, cut onions capture the odours and bacteria of a smelly fridge so cut onions should not be saved, use them or throw them away.

Thyme (optional)
Jar (optional)
Onions
Honey

Take a smallish onion and slice. Add this to about 2–3 tablespoons of honey together with the thyme which can be left on the stalk and allow it to steep for at least 20 minutes. As the juice from the onion seeps into the honey it will become more liquid. Take a tsp every fifteen minutes or as regularly as necessary. The juices form the onion will help to clear the phlegm and the honey and thymes antibacterial qualities will ease a tickly throat. Contraindications: do not use this remedy if the cough is hot and dry as the heat in the onions will only make it worse.

Garlic Soup

This recipe came to me after I had failed to listen to my inner voice that was saying "stop, don't eat that egg, its past it's best". Soft boiled eggs are part of me and my youngest sons Saturday morning ritual. He plays and lets me have a lie on then we breakfast together like kings on soft boiled eggs, tea, toast and kallas kaviar which is a pink salty fish paste from Sweden. So thats what I ate that morning despite my inner voice but an hour later I was feeling decidedly queasy and my guts ached. So I asked the three questions, **How did I feel?** Sick. **What did I need?** Something to make the sickness go, balance the system and kill any internal bacteria SO GARLIC. **How could I love myself more?** Make a soup with tons of garlic. Garlic is a natural antiseptic, antifungal, antibiotic and antioxidant. Here is the result. The following day I added some roasted aubergine and chicken thighs to the soup, cooked it again slowly in the oven and it was a marvellous casserole so, no mistakes just opportunities.

1 tbls butter & 1 tbsp sunflower oil
3 Bulbs of Garlic
1–2 Leeks
2 pints miso stock
450g cooked butter beans or 4/5 medium potatoes
1 tsp ground black pepper

Smash and finely slice 3 bulbs of Garlic, I know it sounds a lot but if they are cooked slowly and softly like caramelized onions they will taste sweet, deep and rich. Heat the butter and oil together, add the garlic and leeks stirring and frying for a minute on a high heat then turn them down very low and add a lid. Cook for about 20 minutes, stirring occasionally. If you are using potatoes rather than beans, add them at this stage tossing them in the garlicky juices for a further 5 minutes before adding the stock and simmering for 20–30

minutes. If using butterbeans add before the soup is ready so they are heated through. Season to taste although be cautious with the salt as miso already has a salty flavour.

Ginger Cookies

Cinnamon, cloves, ginger, nutmeg and cardamom; all the Autumn/Christmas spices have warming expansive qualities and help to counteract cold or damp forming foods such as dairy or sugar. Ginger especially has heating properties which help energy and warmth reach the extremities of the body. It also contains a natural antihistamine which helps reduce inflammation in the body. The Romans would wrap the root of ginger in a piece of bread to aid digestion, hence gingerbread and I used it to soothe my morning and travel sickness. The recipe here is adapted from Heidi Swanson, Super natural every day. I like it because it uses both dried and fresh ginger and is a perfect treat if you fancy something sweet.

230g of spelt wholewheat flour
1 tsp bicarbonate of soda
1½ tbsp ground ginger
½ tsp fine sea salt
115 unsalted butter
60 ml molasses or treacle
100g golden caster sugar
2 tbsp grated fresh ginger
1 large egg, beaten
170g dried apricots finely chopped
75g dark chocolate finely chopped

In a large bowl put the whole wheat flour, bicarb, ground ginger and salt. Melt the butter, molasses, caster sugar and fresh ginger, take off the heat and whisk the egg into the liquid. Then pour over the flour mixture and stir roughly. Right at the end tip in the apricots, chocolate and mix lightly. The dough is easier to work with if you put it in the fridge for 30 minutes but it's not essential. Using a teaspoon take a small lump and work it into a ball, pressing lightly on top. Place on a lined baking tray and put in the oven for 10–15 minutes at 180° C.

The Quickest Hummus Ever

I have picked Hummus here as it is a great alternative to cheese. I had a client who suffered terribly from eczema and when I asked about her diet she was a vegetarian and she ate a cheese sandwich every day. Cheese and other dairy products are notorious for producing mucus and clogging up a damp system so a perfect alternative she could have was hummus — perfect in a wrap with some grated carrot and maybe a few chopped olives if you have them about. If you have a very damp and congested system chick peas are brilliant but you may omit the tahini. I also tend to go heavy on the garlic because it's great for keeping Lungs and Large Intestine healthy and moving and it lasts longer in the fridge.

One tin of chick peas
2 cloves of garlic
1 tsp tahini
Olive oil
Lemon juice
Salt and Pepper to taste,
Sprinkle of paprika (optional)
2-3 tbsp of the chickpea water if it becomes too thick

Put all ingredients in a liquidizer and blitz. You can put all the ingredients in a jug and use a stick blender if you don't have a liquidizer.

Carrageen Moss Jelly/Drink

In the Autumn time our immune system is really under pressure, all seasons can appear in one day which compromises our defences and airborne viruses can enter our system. Carrageen Moss is great at soothing and protecting the lungs and large intestine. It's an age old traditional Irish remedy used for coughs, colds, influenza and even pneumonia. Of course any food which resembles the organ it's treating has to be a winner.

20g Carrageen Moss
1 litre water
Flavour of choice

Rinse the moss clean and place it in a saucepan. Let it soak in the water for 10 minutes and then bring it just to the boil to gently simmer for about 30 minutes until the moss has dissolved. Sometimes not all the moss dissolves so strain it and at this point add the flavour of your choice; perhaps the juice of an orange or a lemon and some honey. My kids like blackcurrant cordial, cookery course participants preferred Barley Malt. Pour it into a mould and leave to set in the fridge or if you want to disguise it further you could add it as a stock to a soup or stew. Often when I'm preparing a vegetable or chicken stock or a big pot of warming stew I rinse a handful and add it to the pot as it's a great thickener. The liquor or jelly depending on how much water you have used will keep in the fridge for a couple of days.

Soap for Psoriasis and Eczema

Whole porridge oats
A sock

Put the oats in a sock. Fill a basin with warm water. Immerse the sock filled with oats, squeeze it a couple of times so that the water runs milky from the sock then use it as soap over the skin. Try running a warm bath with a couple of oat filled socks in it, give it a stir and soak yourself, coming out with silky smooth skin. This is how Cleopatra bathed in milk.

Specific Lung/Large Intestine Points

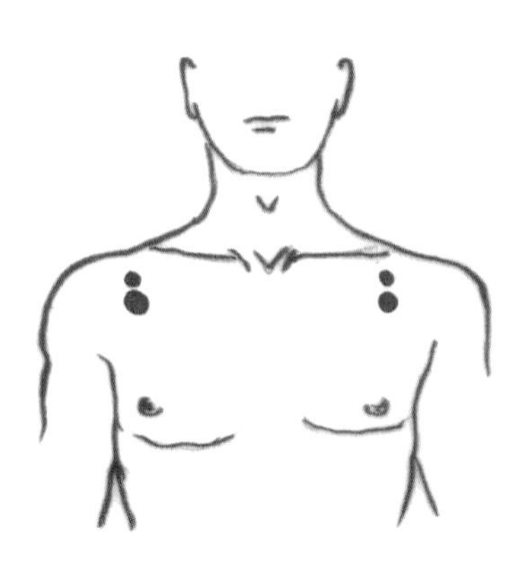

Lu 1 and Lu 2 — connecting. ***Take your fingers along your collar bone, just before the shoulder there is a natural hollow, rub the area three fingers below that and you will connect with Lung 1.*** This can facilitate letting go of grief as it helps to open up the chest and allows vital oxygen to enter the system. It helps to also clasp the hands behind your back further opening the chest and connecting to life. There maybe tears with these points as emotional pain, heartache and sadness is released.

Ll 4 — letting go. ***Rubbing the fleshy web on the upper side of your hand between your thumb and first finger joint you will find a point where the valleys meet.*** This is a powerful point for encouraging the physical and emotional body to let go. So much so it is not a point to be used during pregnancy. However it can alleviate constipation and relieve headaches, including toothaches and sinusitis. It also promotes letting go of tension and grief, leaving the body with a sense of calm.

Specific Lung/Large Intestine Points

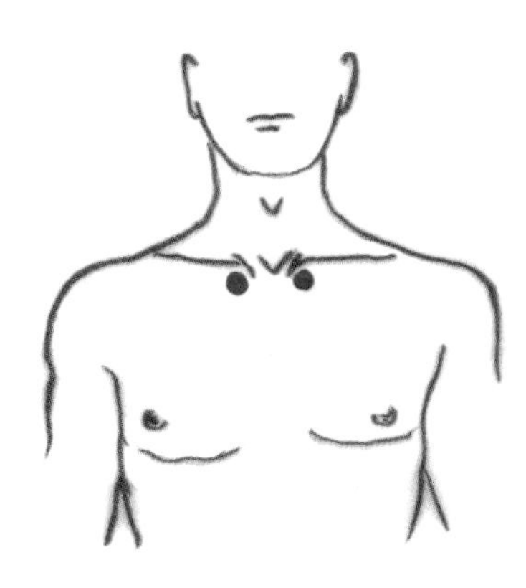

Ki 27 — whole health. ***Take your fingers along your collar bone again but this time come in towards the centre of the body. Where the collar bone meets the sternum allow the fingers to fall just below, into the natural hollow. Rub this area on both sides.*** This is good for any chest congestion, throat problems, chest pain, difficult or shallow breathing. It's a great point for balancing the health, boosting the immune system and increasing the energetic functioning of the whole body.

"Some people believe holding on and hanging in there are signs of great strength. However, there are times when it takes much more strength to know when to let go and then to do it." ***Ann Landers***

Chapter 3: Bladder and Kidney

flavour	salty
season	winter
meridians & organs	bladder & kidney
properties	calm & being
emotion	fear
colour	blue/black

Overview

Today is Blue Monday, perhaps not for you reading but for me writing and it is said to be the saddest day of the year. After the fun time and excitement of holidays are over, I sometimes feel "is this it, is this as good as it gets?" People in my shiatsu practice seem to be restless, dejected and lacking in purpose. So why do we dislike winter and especially January so much?

Winter is the time for Hibernating – for going deep inside, being still and centred. The flowing Water Element governing the Bladder and Kidney are linked to this time of year, the depth of winter, the very marrow of ourselves. This rest time is essential. It is the yin, the quiet time, the absorbing of the natural flow. Under the soil and inside all living organisms nothing is stationary, things are bubbling away. It's a quiet preparation for the action of the year ahead.

The Water element is at our very core and once we have accepted that we don't need to fight or flight, that all is well, our kidneys relax they don't need to do or create anything. There is an understanding that everything is perfect just the way it is. Obviously that doesn't mean you become passionless and inert as even stagnant water smells. For our physical and emotional well being, it is essential to find that yin yang balance between control and going with the flow. Understanding and feeling the Kidney/Bladder energy within the body will help to do that. Even as I type this I can feel my kidneys and my lower back relaxing. I have a list of things I want to do but I know that everything, absolutely everything is as it should be and everything happens effortlessly in its own good time. It's too exhausting if I assume complete control. There is an energetic difference between doing things by personal effort and will power and doing the same things through enjoyment and with the support of a benevolent universe. *If you feel like you are working too hard, pushing yourself or others in any area of your life, you are depleting your kidney/bladder energy.*

Often we use food and drink to give us extra energy to push us on; caffeine being a prime example. There is nothing wrong with tea or coffee but large amounts over a prolonged period of time depletes the kidney/bladder as it stimulates the adrenals and operates as a diuretic. As these organs are at your core of being and form your constitutional energy it is very difficult to replenish this energy when lost. However you can most definitely support them with plenty of rest, salty tasting foods such as seaweeds, dark coloured beans, oats, miso and of course plenty of clean blessed water.

Some Words on Salt

The flavour of the water element is salty, perhaps not unexpectedly as there is a natural affinity between the two. Salts are essential in our bodies for many processes including the transmission of electrical impulses and for the regulation of fluid in the body. However salt is often demonized as being responsible for health problems and certainly taken to excess it can have grave effects. The type of salt that is commonly used is highly refined with added anti caking agents, iodine and sugars. This includes a lot of varieties labelled Sea Salt that really are no better. It is best to search out large greyish, unrefined crystals of whole natural sea salt of Maldon, Brittany or the Himalayas. Salt is a very grounding mineral and so if we are feeling insecure or fearful we can often crave this flavour as subconsciously our body maybe tries to soothe its own fears and help the kidneys to relax. Just as we must find a balance between rest and activity we must find a balance for our salt intake. Be aware that a high meat diet, microwave and other ready meals can have high hidden sodium content. So the recipes in this chapter cover a broad range to give an idea of the variety of places we can find salt and support for our body/mind.

In answer to my own earlier question of why we dislike winter I think there's something about the surrender to this time of year, not only the quietness, the stillness, but the letting go of control that makes us uncomfortable. To trust that things are happening even if we are not making them happen takes support, courage and relaxed kidneys.

Fear is the emotion of the kidneys. We see this in the adrenal glands, situated above the kidneys, which produce adrenaline to help us through extreme situations. It is our fight or flight mechanism. In Chinese medicine the kidney and bladder controls our nervous system. When in fear our body and especially our kidneys contract, our whole nervous system is on edge, whereas when we trust our body relaxes and is at ease. To change from fear to trust just takes a slight shift in perception – relax into your back and your rear brain, instead of focusing on fixing or avoiding the problem think about a solution being produced by the problem. Sounds simple and it is so support your body. Avoid excess stimulants and diuretics. Eat and drink to soothe your nervous system and support your very core. Find a deep peace where your own self settles.

"Rest in natural great peace. This exhausted mind Beaten helpless by karma and neurotic thought. Like the relentless fury of the pounding waves. In the infinite ocean of samsara." ***Nyoshul Khen Rinpoche***

Foods at a glance for Bladder & Kidney

Seaweeds
Wheatgrass
Celery
Corn
Kidney Bean/Aduki Bean
Miso
Barley/Oats
Kudzu
Tamari/Soya sauce

Seeds
Dark fruits blackberry, blueberry
Tofu
Parsley
A balanced diet, as one mineral needs another to function
Good water intake

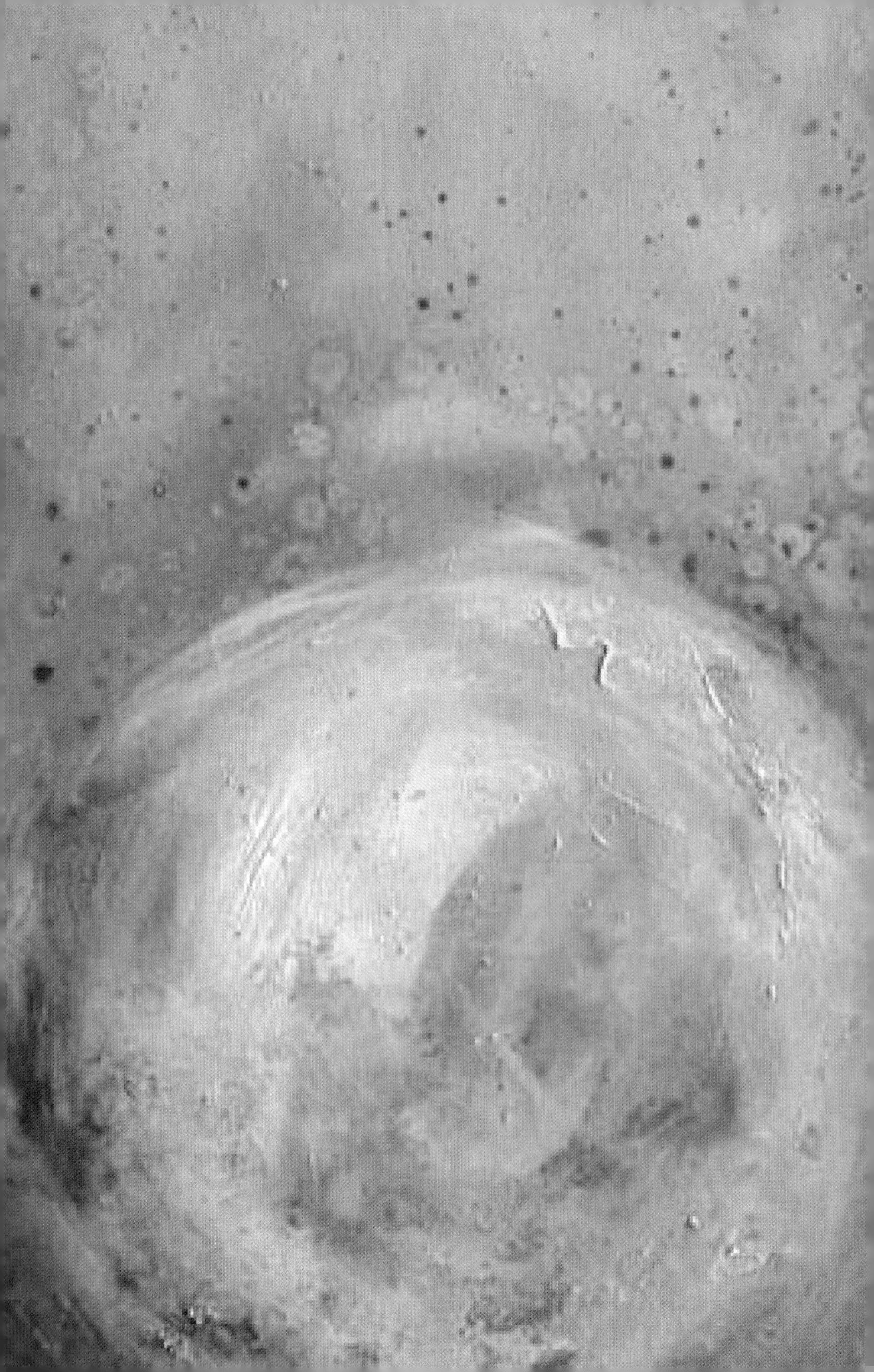

Water Meditation

There is no stopping water and in some ways is the most powerful of all the elements. Think of the strength of a storm or tsunami or the slow quiet trickle as it cuts its way through solid stone. Water is in constant motion travelling down toward sea level, once reached it will start its upward process of precipitation and begin its cycle all over again. Here we will use that image to allow the body to rest in flow.

Sit quietly and comfortably for a few minutes, enjoying all the sounds all around you. If thoughts come, don't think about them, don't solve them, don't follow them. Let them fall like twigs through water or pass as floating clouds; let the mind settle.

With your eyes closed imagine yourself lying by your favourite body of water. It could be an expansive quiet lake, lapping waves on a shore or perhaps a jungle waterfall. Just lie there and listen. As you listen connect with and feel the waters flow and movement. It is powerful and strong yet fluid and soft.

Feel that fluidity as you breathe in. Imagine the water entering through the top of your head and flowing down two channels either side of your spine, down through your hips opening and softening them, down the centre channel of the backs of your legs to the centre of the base of your feet.

As you breathe out that fluid energy travels up the back of your legs, through your hips, up the channels either side of your spine, up over your skull and out of the top of your head. If it helps imagine the water energy as a colour, perhaps bright neon blue surrounded by glowing white. Do this for at least 20 breath's knowing that your spine, hips and legs support you effortlessly and that by allowing this flow, the universe will also support you.

Seaweed and Onion Quiche

Eggs are a great source of protein and as such they boost yin and blood within the body. This dish will fortify that bodybuilder or ballerina within. Eggs can move stagnant energy from the lower regions of the body to moisten the upper areas such as lungs, throat and eyes. However they can cause mucus build up and slow liver function so keep in check with your body to maintain flexibility and flow. I have combined them here with seaweed and caramelized onion, both of which have the ability to transform sticky phlegm so are a great balance with the high dairy content of the quiche. Sometimes if our diet is very protein based our systems can become acidic. Also undue stress means our body produces too much adrenaline which in turn will lead to high acid levels, loss of calcium and osteoporosis. Wakame has exceptionally high levels of calcium to combat bone thinning and onions are an alcalyzing food that can regulate the pH balance in the body.

Pastry
350g plain flour
175 butter
Splashes of ice cold water
Egg for glazing

Filling
125ml milk
125ml cream
4 eggs
Salt & pepper
2 tbsps of oil
Knob of butter
4 red onions
Balsamic vinegar
2 handfulls of dried Wakame or dillisk/dulse
100g of feta

Between finger and thumb, rub the soft butter into the flour and salt until it becomes like sand. To check if it's ready shake the bowl and rub the large lumps that come to the surface. If they are still fatty carry on rubbing keeping it light and airy. When it's ready add a couple of splashes of cold water, with your hands stir the mix into a ball adding more water if you need. However don't let it go sticky if it does sprinkle a little more flour over.

Now let it rest in the fridge for half an hour. If you don't it might shrink in the oven and the contents of the quiche may spill out. Of course you can buy ready made and rolled short crust pastry and if so move straight on – flour a surface and roll out the dough, about 3 millimeters thick and larger than the 30 cm loose bottomed tart case. Roll the pastry loosely around the rolling pin to transport to the case, pressing it gently into place and trim to fit. Cover the pastry with baking paper and fill it with a layer of dried or ceramic beans and bake for 15-20 mins in a preheated oven at 180°. After this time remove the beans and paper and cook for a further 10 mins until the base is golden brown. Use any left over pastry to fix any cracks.

While the pastry is baking, prepare the filling. Melt the oil and butter in a large frying pan, when hot add the onions which have been finely chopped into half moons and let them fry at a high heat for a couple of minutes. Stir them occasionally then turn them down to a medium heat, leave them uncovered and allow them to cook and caramelize which should take anywhere from between 10-20 minutes. At the very end when they are brown and juicy add a splash of balsamic vinegar and allow it to cook in for a couple of minutes. To prepare the seaweed allow it to soak in water for 10 minutes to rehydrate. Then chop it roughly into small bite size pieces.

To assemble the quiche spread the onions and seaweed onto the base of the cooked pastry case, crumble evenly the feta on top and then slowly pour on the custard mix which has been beaten together in a jug. Try not to move around your carefully arranged onions and feta; it should be evenly distributed throughout the quiche. A good tip is to fill the quiche as it sits on the baking shelf in the oven to prevent transportation thrills and spills. Bake the quiche for 30 minutes at 180° until the centre is set. Allow it five minutes to settle down before you remove from the tin and eat.

Seaweed and
Onion Quiche

Miso and Kudzu Soup

I couldn't write this chapter without mentioning miso as a standard ingredient for supporting kidney/bladder. It is a fermented product made from either soybean (hatcho), barley (mugi) or rice (kome). It contains lactobacillus, a great bacteria for the large intestine. Traditionally, in China, it is used to bring good health and long life by ensuring strong kidneys. The kidney/bladder covers the skeletal system and neurological function of the body, which also covers nails and hair. So swap that café latté for a cup of miso for a relaxed smile, lustrous healthy hair and strong nails.

1–2 tsp. miso
Sprinkle dried wakame seaweed
100ml boiling water
1 spring onion
Sprinkle of sesame seeds

Over cooking of miso will damage the beneficial bacteria so boil the water with the seaweed and spring onion for a minute, take off the heat, dissolve in the miso paste, sprinkle on sesame seeds before pouring into a bowl or cup to drink. Add the amount of miso you desire to taste although be aware that too much of the hearty salty tasting miso can exacerbate weakening conditions. Wakame is especially good for softening hard masses within the body and counteracting growths and tumours. Sesame seeds, especially black are renowned for supporting yin and strengthening the kidneys, even darkening prematurely greying hair. Kudzu is the dried root of the long daikon radish. By dissolving a teaspoon of the white powder into one tablespoon of cold water and adding to the soup, along with the miso for a minute, will thicken the soup and increase the fortifying kidney properties.

Japanese Aduki Bean Stew

This delicious recipe is adapted from "Recipes for Self-Healing" by Daverick Leggett. I think it's perfect served with some chewy brown rice and steamed green broccoli during the icy cold months or with the Cucumber Salad if times are warmer. During winter months we crave long cooked beans, hot soups and stews. They take their time to release their heat and energy into our body, giving a feeling of grounding and strength. Unless you have a greenhouse, or buy it in a bag, gone are the days of quick growing lettuce and tender leaves, which are predominantly Yin foods; they grow quickly and their energy is dispersed and used rapidly. During Winter months we need yang foods which are generally condensed or small in size and take a long time to grow, such as beans, seeds, barley and millet. The longer and slower they are cooked for, the longer and slower their energy release will be, ensuring we are kept cozy and supported from the inside.

In this recipe I have used aduki beans which are small and brown but any small dark bean is great to support the kidney/bladder. The way in which you cook your food impacts on the energy you will receive from the food so with this in mind it is best to soak and cook your own beans. However in these busy times I have been known to open a tin or two myself. It's not too difficult to pre-soak and cook it just means planning your meal ahead. Try soaking them the evening before and in the morning rinse and cook so they are ready for the evening meal. Do not salt the beans as this makes their skins very tough, instead add a strip of Kombu seaweed to the water. Even a small amount can have real benefits. All sea vegetables are a fabulous source of vitamins minerals and amino acids. Within the body seaweed breaks down hardened deposits therefore they are also great at breaking down hard beans. Carrageen whilst a brilliant food for the lung and large intestine, is not good to add at this stage as it is a thickening agent and will slow down the cooking. Bring the water with the beans to the boil then simmer for approximately 40–60 minutes taking any foam off the surface with a slotted spoon. Strain the beans, the liquor of which can be drunk warm or cold a tonic for the kidney/bladder.

500g Cooked Aduki Beans
6 Dried Shitake Mushrooms
500ml Dashi Broth
1 Butternut Squash
1 medium sweet potato
2 tablespoons soya sauce
1 teaspoon freshly grated ginger
1 tablespoon honey
Freshly ground black pepper

So with the beans cooked begin the stew. Make the Dashi broth by soaking the dried shitake mushrooms for 30 minutes in 500ml water from a recently boiled kettle. Meanwhile peel and chop the squash and sweet potato into fairly small pieces. Following the soaking, slice finely the mushrooms and combine with Aduki beans, squash, sweet potato, dashi broth, soya sauce and ginger. Simmer them all together slowly until the liquid has reduced by at least half, the squash and sweet potato are soft and the flavors have condensed. Take it off the heat, add the honey and black pepper, letting them melt into this beautiful, colourful stew.

Corn Bread with Feta and Walnuts

Polenta is a great accompaniment to dishes as it is plain and mildly diuretic to counterbalance any dampness by the richness of a meal. It's a great underused alternative to wheat or potato. In this recipe I have added walnuts and feta cheese. Feta further supports kidney/bladder with is salty flavour and walnuts have a specific effect on the neurological function of the brain which is also under the realm of kidney/bladder. This bread is fantastic served warm straight from the oven and as it's so simple to put together that you can astound with freshly baked bread.

150g Polenta
75g wholegrain spelt flour
4 tsp baking powder
1 tsp salt
2 eggs
200ml soya milk
1 tbsp sunflower oil
1 tbsp maple syrup
Handful of coarsely chopped walnuts
50g feta cheese

In a bowl combine the dry ingredients, polenta, spelt, baking powder and salt. Polenta can be bought as a very grainy mix or a fine cornmeal flour. Often I like to mix the two for soft bread with a little texture. In a jug mix the soya milk, sunflower oil, maple syrup, feta and walnuts. Then add the wet to the dry and stir, pour into a buttered loaf tin and bake for 45 minutes at 170° degrees.

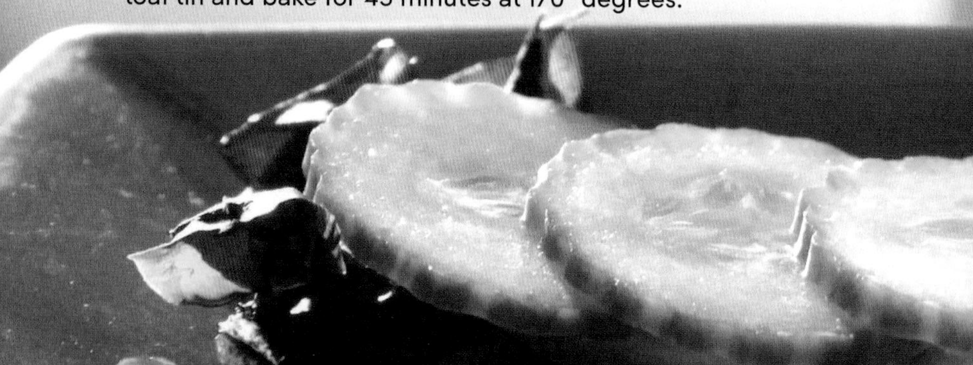

Cucumber and Dillisk Seaweed Salad

Cucumber is a naturally cooling food but the purpose of this recipe is the seaweed. The taste for this time of year is salty and the best way to get this flavour is sea vegetables which are incredibly rich in minerals often missing in our diet due to decline in soil quality. Dillisk/Dulse is said to have over 200 times more iron than green leafy land vegetables. It is exceptionally high in iodine and manganese which is great for keeping our digestive enzymes and metabolism in smooth running order.

15g (large handful Dillisk/Dulse
1 Cucumber
Sprinkle of seasalt and sesame seeds
Freshly squeezed Orange Juice

Soak the dillisk in the orange juice for ten minutes, meanwhile slice the cucumber paper thin and place between paper towels with a weight such as a breadboard on top to press out some of the fluid. Return to the seaweed which should now be soft, take it out of the orange juice and finely chop as if it were an herb. Toss this through the pressed cucumber and serve as a fresh accompaniment to the warming vegetable curry or yummy in a chicken sandwich.

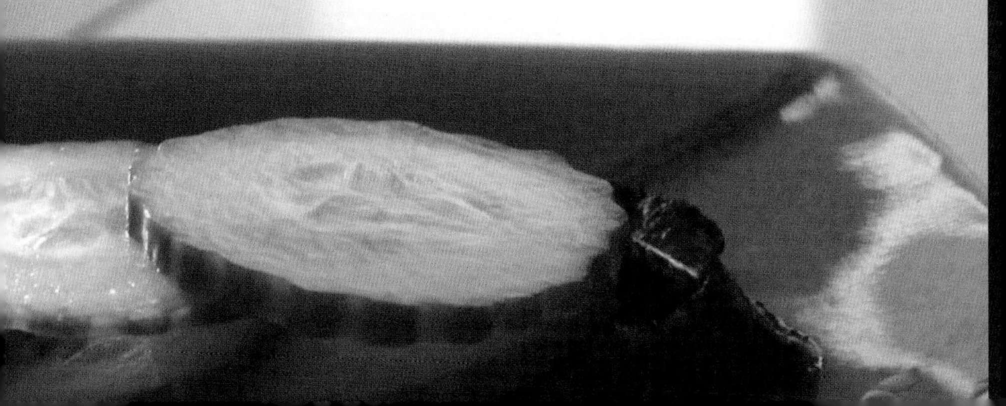

Porridge My Favourite Way

I know it seems silly to have a simple recipe for porridge but oats are a great remedy for frazzled nerves. Their warmth and comfort really bring the body home. This is because they supply the body with melatonin, a hormone produced by the pineal gland located at the centre of the brain. This can be taken as a supplement and is sometimes known as the "jet lag pill" as it aids the body's natural relaxed body clock. However, if taken as a supplement regularly the body can become dependant upon it, rather have a bowl of porridge. However if you are constantly stressed porridge cannot cure this. You may want to look at lifestyle changes to address the causes of stress rather than eating vats of porridge to reduce the affects of stress. Stress cannot be underestimated and I believe is a large reason for dis-ease and sickness in the body. It compromises the natural flow of energy; it blocks neurological and hormonal function. It affects digestion and therefore causes vulnerable areas in the body which are a space for pathogens to enter or deposits to build. The body overheats and uses our precious energy unnecessarily. We need literally to chill out. Stop being over concerned with achieving things or finishing things. Leave the world to look after itself whilst you look after yourself and go make some porridge.

3-4 handfuls of rolled oats per person

220ml water

1 apple cox, gala or similar

Peel, core and chop small eating apple, add a little water to the saucepan and with medium heat begin to soften the apples. After a couple of minutes add the porridge oats and remaining water, stir together and simmer for approximately 5 minutes until the oats are soft and gooey. Golden syrup is my favourite topping although barley malt is much better for the Bladder and Kidney, full of vitamins, iron and good for releasing stress.

Miracle Chicken Soup

The first step here is to make a chicken stock. Stock made from the essence of any bones or vegetables is great for the bladder and kidney. It is the very core, the marrow that we are extracting, it will feed and nurture us, in the same way. This type of stock has been used for centuries, by many different cultures, to build up the strength of the frail and weak. Here we add coconut milk to further strengthen the chi and gentle spices to warm the lung/large intestine.

2 tbsp olive oil
5 shallots or 2 red onions
3 cloves garlic
1 tablespoon fresh ginger
¼ tsp chilli
½ tsp turmeric
½ shredded Chinese cabbage
2 medium carrots cut into sticks
1 chopped celery stalk
2 litres chicken stock
1 tin coconut milk
1-2 sticks of fresh lemon grass
2 handfuls of green beans or mange tout
Bean/mungbean sprouts (optional)
Fresh coriander to garnish

Take the carcass and bones that are left over from a meal (cooked or uncooked) add to these 2 onions, a stick of celery, a big carrot, 3 cloves of garlic, some peppercorns, a tablespoon of miso, two bay leaves, a generous sprinkling of sea salt and 3 litres of water. Some extra uncooked chicken wings will really boost the flavour but they are not essential. Bring to the boil and then allow to simmer softly with the lid on for about 2 hours. The slightly acidic vegetables help to bring out the nutrients of the bones and their marrows. A tablespoon of lemon juice will also do the same. The liquid will have reduced and once strained should produce about two litres of stock. As you are using the very essence of the animal/vegetable it is important to use the highest quality possible. No one wants to eat the essence of an unhappy animal, so free range is a must, organic if you can. Take a large pot and heat the oil, gently fry the shallots or red onions for 5 minutes so they are soft and golden then add the garlic, ginger, turmeric and chilli and fry for a further 5 minutes ensuring the garlic and turmeric do not burn. Pop in the carrot and celery and allow to sweat for another five minutes. Then add the lemongrass, stock and coconut milk bring to a simmer but do not allow to boil. Just as the vegetables are beginning to soften (about 10 minutes) add the shredded Chinese leaves, green beans and sprouts and cook for another couple of minutes. Sprinkle with some chopped coriander, serve and feel the soup warming and strengthening from the inside out.

Anzac Oat Cookies

125g white spelt flour
60g caster sugar or raw cane sugar
100g oats
80g shredded coconut
20g ground almonds
125 butter
2 tbsp golden syrup
½ tsp bicarbonate of soda

These biscuits were used during WW2 and sent to the soldiers at the front because they were full of energy and hearty ingredients. Eggs were on ration so this recipe contains none. Mix all dry ingredients into a bowl. Melt the syrup and butter together until they begin to bubble like toffee. Disolve the bicarbonate of soda in 1 tablespoon of cold water and add to the bubbling mixture. Stir it as it froths up. Then add to the dry mix waiting in the bowl. Squeeze the mixture into smallish egg shapes and then squash with your hand until they flatten slightly. This mix makes about 15 biscuits. Bake for approx 20 mins at 180 until they turn a golden brown.

Sushi Nori Rolls

Sushi is great to make a tupperware full and then store in the fridge using as additions to lunch boxes or quick snacks. Great *wow factor* finger food at parties too. With the protein from the seaweed, the carbohydrate from the rice and the various flavour fillings it can be a highly balanced and complete meal. It takes me the same amount of time to make a sandwich as it does to make a sushi roll. Tricky at first but persevere. Where ever possible I add seaweed to my diet. Even small amounts are extremely beneficial. Sea plants contain many more minerals and vitamins compared to plants grown on land. All seaweeds aid detoxification of the body and improve water metabolisation. Just a few of their direct medicinal benefits are that they cleanse the lymphatic system, lower fat and cholesterol in the blood, aid thyroid operation, reduce swellings in the body and improve the intestinal tract. Nori is a seaweed that is sold in most supermarkets and is very versatile. It has the highest protein of all the seaweeds and is very easily digested. Its benefits medicinally are that it reduces cholesterol and other fatty deposits in the body including fatty cysts under the skin. It's great at relieving painful urination and water retention. Another recipe idea is to crisp the sheet over a flame or in the oven and then crumble into salads or over grains.

Fillings:
Avocado/Tuna
Red pepper/Cucumber
Smoked salmon/Tofu /Omlette

Sushi rice
Nori sheets
Sushi rolling mat
Dipping sauce

Cook the sushi rice as directed on the packet. It should be soft and sticky. Allow it to cool slightly before rolling. While the rice is cooking prepare the fillings. Some of my favourites are sliced omelette with roasted red pepper and tinned tuna with pickled ginger. For the dipping sauce mix two tablespoons of soya sauce with half a tablespoon of horseradish sauce. Now to assemble, lay the nori sheet shiny side down onto the sushi rolling mat. A third of the way up the nori sheet lay a horizontal column of rice approximately 2.5 cm wide, make a groove down the centre of the rice into which lay your filling. Pick up the matt closest to you and begin to roll the seaweed over the top of the rice. Roll it tight and tuck the seaweed edge closest to you under the rice and continue to roll like a cigar. When you reach the far side, moisten with water and press gently through the matt to ensure it seals. You can store these sushi cigars until ready to eat. Then take a sharp knife, keeping the blade wet and clean to ensure a neat cut, slice the roll into six or eight pieces.

Baked Apple

This was tricky — where to put this recipe — Apples are great; great at cooling and moistening the lungs, great at clearing the digestive tract and great for flushing the gall bladder. The pectin within apples can remove cholesterol, toxic metals and residues of radiation. But I decided to put it here because on a cold night after a big meal it's great to have this comforting dessert. Whilst warm and nourishing this is light enough that it won't interfere with the digestion of the main meal. The cinnamon and zest will also promote internal movement and warmth. Usually when I make these I make about eight because they are great as a sweet snack from the fridge.

6 Medium sized eating Apples
50g Butter
50g Dried apricots and raisins
1 tsp Dried Cinnamon
Zest of 1 Orange or Lemon
2 Cinnamon Sticks
100ml Apple Juice

Firstly chop the dried fruit and bind it together with the butter, cinnamon and zest. Then de-core the apple and stuff the butter mixture into the empty core. Sit them on a tray, pouring the apple juice around them and scattering the cinnamon stick in the apple juice. Cover the tray loosely with tin foil and bake for about 45 minutes at 170°, great with a dollop of vanilla yogurt.

Barley Water

Barley has a similar calming neurological effect as oats but also works specifically on the urinary system. It is an internal antiseptic, flushing out any bacteria that can cause infection and cooling inflamed channels therefore alleviating painful urination. Cooked whole barley also works on the intestines to improve bowel function, if you wish to treat diarrhoea, dry roast the barley before adding water and cooking.

50g barley (preferably not pearlized)
2 pints water
Lemon Juice/Barley Malt or Honey

Pinch of Salt

Put a heavy based saucepan on the heat, add the barley, water and salt. Bring this to the boil then reduce to a low rolling simmer. Put the lid on and leave to simmer for at least an hour making sure that it does not dry out. Strain the liquid, to which you can add lemon juice, a natural sweetener or both. This will keep in the fridge for a few days and I find it helpful to use it almost as a concentrate, adding boiling water and lemon when I want a calming hot drink.

Celery Tonic

2 tbsp of celery seeds
100ml water
100ml honey

Traditionally celery is said to calm the nerves and this is probably because it has very high calcium levels. It is a mild diuretic, good at relieving arthritis and rheumatic disorders. I like to think of it as keeping all the fluids moving, sweeping away any debris meaning no dams or blockages that create swellings. The seeds are high in vitamins A, B and C and can help reduce high blood pressure. For a kidney tonic, try crushing celery seeds and mixing with honey and water. Take 2 tablespoons of the honey water 3 times daily. As celery may cause the uterus to contract is advised not to eat celery during pregnancy.

Specific Bladder/Kidney Points

Kidney 1 — ***for grounding, stability and connection to the universal energy.*** Press on the sole of your foot just on the inside corner of the ball of the foot.

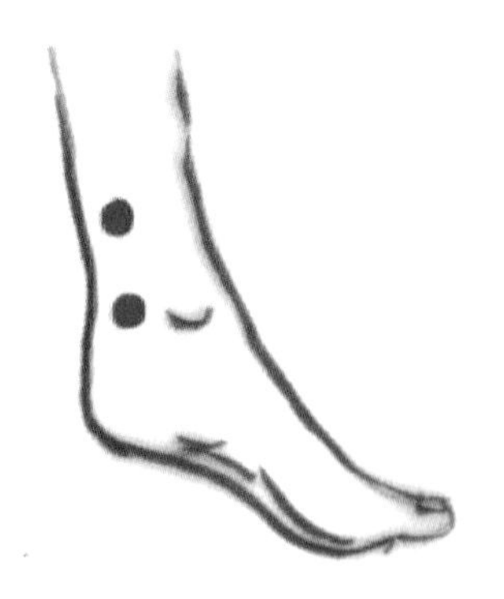

Kidney 3-7 — ***alleviating back pain brought on by overuse of will power to push on through.*** Pinch and massage the back of the ankle and Achilles tendon. Massage and squeeze from the Achilles tendon up the back of the leg to just before the beginning of the calf muscle.

Specific Bladder/Kidney Points

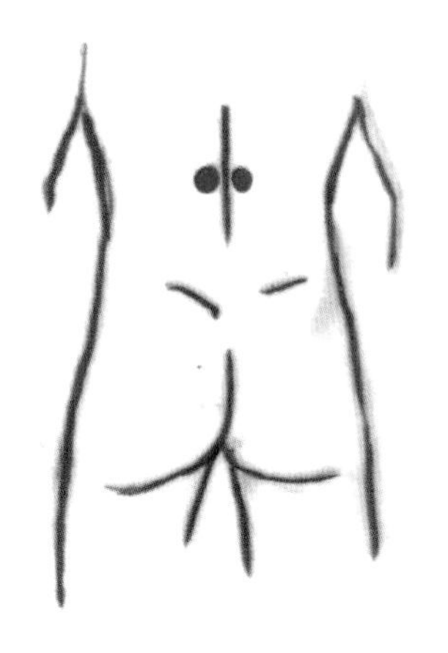

Bladder 23 — ***relax and melt away fears.*** Put your hands on hips, reversed so the thumbs are to the front and the fingers are splayed on the back, move the fingers up and down the muscle either side of the spine or make the hands into gentle fists and rub up and down the muscles up and down the spine, knowing and feeling the warmth and support of a benevolent universe.

Kidney 27 — ***align and tonify energy.*** Trace your finger along your collarbone/clavicle until you reach the beginning of your breastbone, just under the collar bone at that point is an indentation which is K 27. Press and rotate on this point to relax the chest, descend any energy rebellious lung and stomach chi, calm the adrenals and balance the overall energy in your body.

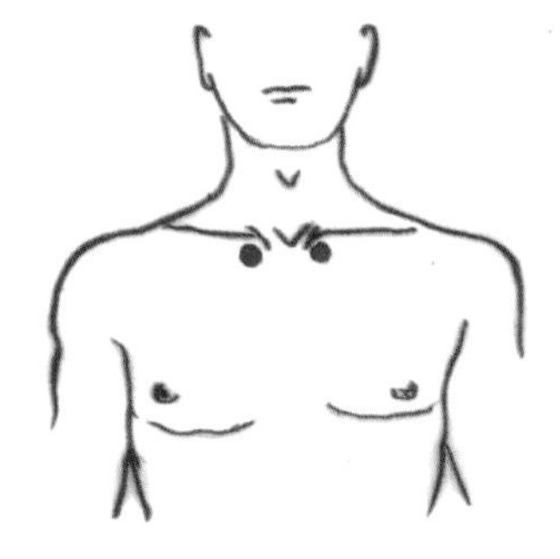

Chapter 4: Liver and Gall Bladder

flavour	sour
season	spring
meridians & organs	liver & gall bladder
properties	dynamic, flexible, effective
emotion	anger, creativity
colour	green

Overview

Today is a windy day in May. The daffodils and tulips of early Spring are gone but everything is green and still growing. The small shoots have pushed through the soil, the clematis has wound around canes and the peonies are bursting through their casing with an intensity of colour. Winter is over, its time to wake up and move. This is the energy of the season, flexible and vibrant, full of new potential. The organs paired to this energy are the Liver and Gall Bladder.

The Liver is the only organ within the body able to regenerate. No matter how diseased it becomes it always has the potential to grow again. Just like the new shoots in spring, it is irrepressible in its desire for life. Gotta love the liver!

In Chinese Medicine the function of the Liver is to nourish, purify and store the blood. It also keeps the chi (energy) moving around the body. Just like the new shoots of spring are able to move around stones and obstacles, our energy and blood, if the liver is functioning properly, will move around the body easily without obstruction. However in our western lifestyle it is very easy to overwork the liver. Too many saturated fats, chemical additives, alcohol, caffeine and stimulants make the liver slow so leading to "stagnation" in the system. To help the liver we can use the sour flavour. If I think of an oily surface, nothing cuts through better than the juice of a lemon. Pickles and relishes pick up the heaviness of fatty hamburgers or best of all, greasy yummy fish and chips always come with a heavy dose of vinegar. These taste combinations are all the bodies' way at helping itself. In relation to the liver it needs to stay flowing and flexible. If it can't work well things become stuck and obstructed. Physically this may manifest as swelling or build up deposits of toxins in the body or on the skin. So just as Spring is traditionally a time for cleaning up so too it is beneficial for a clear out of the liver. Detoxs don't have to be radical to be effective simply eating less meat for a week will have an amazing effect.

The Liver's partner, the Gall Bladder, creates bile which assists in the breaking down of fats in the liver. Green plants full of chlorophyll help the Gall Bladder make this "pure" fluid which never enters or leaves the body. So munch Spring greens for a couple of weeks and see how easy it is to touch your toes.

A liver in balance means clear decisions, as the energy in your body is not obstructed. You have clarity and are flexible, undeterred by obstacles, moving forward with grace and ease. However out of balance these obstacles can cause undue frustration and anger. Anger is a tricky emotion in the west. I'm all for a bit of anger if it is used appropriately and does not escalate to violence. Sometimes it is a necessary energy to clear out things from the system, however if it is used with too much force and too often, it is detrimental to ones body and mind. If anger is suppressed and not allowed its flow then it can turn inwards creating depression and stagnation. For me the following famous quote teams the physical and emotional energy of the Liver/Gall Bladder perfectly. An essential balance of Yin Yang for a flowing life...

God grant me the serenity to accept the things I cannot change, courage to face the things I can and Wisdom to know the difference."

Liver Meditation

Sit either cross legged on a cushion of with your feet on the floor in a kitchen chair, either way ensure you are comfortable and that your back is reasonably straight. Now close your eyes, take 5 deep breaths every time breathing further and further into the point just behind and below your navel. Now let the breath go and feel all the tension drain away from your muscles in your face in your shoulders, down your arms, around your chest, in your belly, down your spine, its all draining out of your body like water in rivulets down your legs and out through your toes. Now through the point in the very top of your head breathe and draw in glowing white light. Breathe this light in four times whilst at the same time feeling the tension drain from your face and cheeks out through your toes.

Now imagine you have a doorway in the middle of your chest. With your eyes closed imagine the door opening and in the space behind the door is your favourite flower or plant. Still with your eyes closed feel that plant in that space behind the door and breathe in the green of that chamber. Keep breathing the green; imagine it spreading throughout the body just like blood vessels. It's everywhere, curling down your legs, twisting around your toes, spiralling through sockets of your eyes until you are a ball of green. Sit in that ball of green just as the plant within you is blown by the breeze you too are flexible and full of vibrant energy. Sit until you feel every part of your body tingling with the supple green then let it go, let it dissipate and for a minute just sit and feel how the body feels, keep softening, keep smiling.

Foods at a glance for Liver & Gall Bladder

Sprouted seeds
and legumes
Good oils in seeds
nuts & fish
Aubergines
Fresh & raw food

Lemon & limes
Pickles & cider vinegar
Plums & gooseberries
Nettles, spring onions,
kale, spinach & broccoli

Warm Tangy Barley

I first created this recipe in response to a client who was being woken during he night to urinate. The barley in this recipe will strengthen the kidney essence, especially if you replace the pumpkin seeds for walnuts. But here I want to use the kale and spinach to increase the chlorophyll intake. This boosts the Gall Bladder into producing bile which helps the liver breakdown fats and rid the body of unwanted waste materials. The seeds bring all the right omega 3 and 6 oils to support the liver, however careful not to overdo seeds, they can be heavy on the system. Listen to your body wisdom.

1 head of Kale
2 tbsp sunflower oil
200 barley (or 100g barley & 100g brown rice
70–100g toasted pumkin seed/pine nuts
2 tbsp sesame seeds
100g strong blue cheese

Whole/pot barley is best to use here, as the more commonly used pearl barley has less fibre, calcium and iron. Most health food shops stock whole/pot barley. To cook add the barley to approximately 1½ litres of water, bring to the boil and simmer for 45 minutes. When the barley is soft, strain off and keep the liquor (see page 80). Pour the barley into a lovely large serving bowl, stir in the spinach so that it wilts and cover to keep warm.

Next set your oven high 190-200° and pour the sunflower oil on a large baking tray and place back in the oven. Meanwhile strip the dark green kale from the pale stalks, wash and chop roughly. Toss the chopped kale on the tray in the hot oil from the oven. Put the tray of kale back in the oven and roast for about 5 minutes. Check on it as it crisps up quickly. It may need a shuffle and another 5 minutes roasting. Once it is crispy, shower it with sea salt, sesame seeds and place in the bowl of barley.

Toast the pumpkin seeds in the oven at the same time as the kale in a dry flat roasting tin, giving them a shake after a couple of minutes to make sure they don't stick or burn. When they are ready they will look shiny and smell divine. Toss them to the bowl of roasted kale and soft barley, adding the optional blue cheese and the Umeboshi dressing on the following page.

Umeboshi Dressing

Umeboshi plum is a very sour traditional Japanese ingredient used to settle the stomach, alkalize the system and calm the liver. It can be bought as a vinegar or a paste. It is brilliant in small amounts to clear and support the liver but just like Yin and Yang, if you use it too much it can have the opposite effect. Rather than trying to constantly cure an overworked liver be conscious about the food you eat. Better to address the cause rather than the symptom.

1 tbsp umeboshi vinegar
1 tbsp sesame oil
1 tsp Dijon mustard
60ml rice or cider vinegar
Juice of 1 orange or 1 lemon if you prefer tangy
50ml olive oil

This dressing is great over any green vegetables and you can add herbs such as tarragon or coriander to beef it up. Simply place all the ingredients into a jar, put the lid on, hold the jar, dance around the kitchen, shake vigorously and express yourself. Feel that energy of youth that wants to burst out into the world.

Rich Smoked Mackerel Pate

If cell walls become too rigid, fats and toxins can accumulate within the cell. To promote flexibility and movement at a cellular level, we must eat plenty of essential fatty acids. Oily fish such as sardines, herring, tuna, pilchards, salmon and mackerel, contain high levels of these fatty acids are great for supporting the liver in its job of moving debris from the blood and assisting detox at this cellular level. The aubergines are particularly effective at clearing blood stagnation in the lower area of the body and especially in the uterus. I recommend roasting an aubergine whenever possible. If you have the oven on, pierce the aubergine with the tip of a sharp knife as you would a baked potato, wrap in tin foil and place on a baking tray. It will take about 45 minutes to become soft like butter inside. Scoop out the flesh with a spoon, taking care not to get too much of the black skin which can be bitter. This will keep in a tupperware in the fridge for up to 5 days. I usually add it to curries and stews for rich flavour, whilst at the same time knowing I am fortifying and regulating blood movement.

2 cloves of garlic
Juice of 2 lemons
Large handful of flat leaf parsley
Salt and pepper to taste
4 (2lb) medium roasted aubergines
1lb smoked mackerel fillets
½ lb spread cheese
2 tbsp olive oil

To make this pate is exceptionally easy. De-skin and bone the fish, take the scooped out innards of the aubergine and mix together with the cream cheese, yogurt, olive oil and lemon juice. Smash and finely chop the garlic with the parsley and add to the mixture. You can combine with a blender for a very smooth texture but I like to mash it all together with a fork so that it retains a chunky quality and the parsley has some crunch.

White Fish with Caponata

This sounds or reads like a very odd recipe but cook it and see. It keeps for days in the fridge and just gets better with age. The tangy relish flavour makes it a perfect accompaniment to fish, the oilier fish the better to soothe the often overworked Liver.

2 onions
1 aubergine
1 red pepper
1 green pepper
2 stalks of celery
1 bulb of fennel
4oz green beans
½ lb of mushrooms
1 lb tomatoes
6 cloves garlic
½ cup olive oil
½ cup balsamic vinegar
1 cup black olives
2 tbsp capers
½ cup fresh basil
salt and pepper

In a large heavy based pan, use half of the olive oil to fry the onions on a medium heat until soft and golden. Then add all the vegetables, which have been chopped quite small, the rest of the oil and balsamic vinegar. Cook uncovered on a very low heat for about an hour until all the liquid has been absorbed or has evaporated. Then add the chopped olives, capers, herbs and seasoning to taste and cook for another 5 minutes.

For the white fish take a fillet of haddock or cod and set the oven for 170°. Run your finger over the flesh of the fish to check for bones but leave the skin on. Place the fish on a piece of tin foil in a baking tray and drizzle with olive oil and lemon juice. Season with salt and pepper then fold up the sides of the tin foil and wrap together creating a parcel so that the steam can circulate within as it bakes. Leave in the oven for about 10–15 minutes until the fish becomes chunky flakes.

Spring Green Soup

This soup has a great colour, an incredible vibrant green of the Shrek variety (if you are careful not to overcook the kale). Green is the colour of Spring and of Liver/Gall Bladder. All dark green foods help the gall bladder excrete bile which breaks down fat. The recipe is an adaptation from Davrick Leggits "Recipes for Self Healing" in which he uses nettles. Nettles and Milk Thistle are popular effective herbal tonics for the liver. Here I have substituted the nettles for Kale. However if you wish to have a go pick young nettle tops which are best gathered in spring and use just as kale.

1 onion
1 clove of garlic
Knob of butter
1 head of kale or 2 heads of york cabbage
100g of spinach
3 or 4 medium peeled potatoes
2 pints veg stock
1 tsp nutmeg
juice of 1 lemon
salt and pepper

Cook the onions in the butter on a medium heat until golden and soft add the garlic and sliced potatos (I like to cut mine into round disks). Stir softly for 5 minutes ensuring all ingredients are coated. Add the kale and a couple of tablespoons of stock and let all ingredients sweat for 5 minutes. Then add the rest of the stock and cook for about 10 minutes until the potatoes are soft but not crumbling. Remove the potatoes and liquidize the remaining stock and kale in the pan, adding the nutmeg, lemon, seasoning and a couple of handfuls of spinach if you want extra green. Return the potatoes to the pot and it's done. Even though the sour flavour is part of the purpose of this liver nourishing soup, careful that it does not overpower the earthy warmth of the soup.

Stewed Plum & Rhubarb

There is a condition called Plum Pit Qi which is when you feel you have something lodged, like a plum stone, in your throat. In Chinese medicine this blockage would indicate a problem with self expression and therefore stagnant liver energy. Anti depressants are sometimes prescribed for the condition in the west but medicating a condition brought about through an inability to express oneself can exacerbate the problem by suppressing feelings even deeper. If we imagine the problem as a wall, when standing with your face pressed up against the wall, it feels frustrating and overwhelming; no options, no way forward and no exit. However if I take a few steps back I can see that it is not a wall at all but simply a large pillar I can walk around. I can be flexible if I have a better perspective. A healthy liver/gall bladder helps that discernment and perspective. However when these organs are under stress instead of feeling the flexibility they can get stuck in the frustration. Depression is that anger turned inward, that inability or futility to express oneself. Medication as discussed before can be beneficial in some cases but physically it puts the liver under stress and it can also bury that frustration deeper. Find something to aid liver function that helps to express who you are, keep a journal, talk to a councillor, join an art or dance class. Feel yourself as a vibrant individual who is doing their thing, an essential part of the human race.

1 lb plums & 1 lb of rhubarb
½ tsp fennel seeds
½ tsp dried ginger
500ml apple juice
1 tbsp of apple juice concentrate

Stone and halve the plums. Put the apple juice in a heavy based pan followed by the spices and the plums. I put the seeds in a tea strainer because I don't like the texture but fennel seeds are great for the digestion when chewed.

Bring almost to the boil and allow to gently simmer for 10-15 minutes, depending on how mushy you like your plums. This is great eaten warm with a dollop of vanilla yogurt.

Sprouts and How to Sprout

Fresh sprouts are at the beginning of their growth, all their potential for becoming a fully grown plant is just being released from the seed. Their proteins and sugars are being broken down by the germination process which makes it really easy for our body to digest. Eating sprouts on a regular basis will mean we feel full of the joys of spring — literally as these foods are the most attuned to that energy. There are many seeds, grains and legumes that can be sprouted and there are many methods to sprout them. Here I share what I think is the easiest seed to sprout in the easiest way.

Take 1 tablespoon of Alfalfa seeds and soak them in a jug of water for 8 hours. I usually put them to soak the evening before I want to begin sprouting. In the morning rinse the seeds and lay them out, fairly evenly on thick kitchen paper towel. Take a large tupperware and fill it with a centimetre of water. Place the kitchen towel flat in the tupperware. The paper towel should absorb the water and be thoroughly saturated although the seeds should not themselves be swimming in water. Cover the tupperware with a tea towel and place somewhere dark and warm. Rinse the seeds and replace the paper towel twice a day, once in the morning, once in the evening. After a couple of days they will have begun to sprout and after four days they should be ready to eat. If you want to increase the chlorophyll content uncover and leave near indirect sunlight for another couple of days, continuing to rinse. Washed and stored in a bag or covered container these sprouts will keep up to a week.

A Word or Two on Arthritis

Rheumatoid arthritis is a very painful and complex condition.

It is caused by the body attacking itself and causing inflammation most commonly between the joints of fingers, toes, knees and ankles. It can have different causes and a variety of symptoms in every person, however encouraging flow within the body often helps the condition. The steroid based prescribed medication can exacerbate the condition by creating cold stagnation within the body. So keep up movement with chlorophyll intake; plenty of lightly steamed greens and plenty of lubricating oils through seeds, nuts and fish. Pineapple contains bromelain which can sometimes act as an anti-inflammatory for the swollen joints. Food can sometimes aggravate the condition so I would recommend working with a dietary practitioner to compliment rather than dismiss conventional medicine.

Lemon Juice

Lemons have so many benefits for the body. They are rich in vitamins B and C. They are a natural antiseptic, destroying putrefactive bacteria in the intestines and the mouth. They are also great at halting the flow of blood and infection when used externally on the skin. Having a high potassium content also makes them useful as a tonic for the heart. However in this section their sour flavour is perfect for the liver and gall bladder. It encourages the production of bile which as already discussed is essential for a high-fat or protein rich western diet. The citric acid thins the blood improving circulation, reducing stagnation at the same time improving the absorption of minerals and detoxification of the blood. A simple way to take lemon is to squeeze a quarter of lemon into a cup and add some recently boiled water. If you wish a stronger lemon drink slice three lemons into 1 pint of water and boil until the liquid has reduced by half. Honey can be added to taste. 2 tablespoons of lemon juice mixed with 2 tablespoons of olive oil taken on an empty stomach help to dissolve gall stones which leads us on to the next recipe.

The Gall Bladder Flush and Detoxing the System

There are many variations on this theme, almost like an urban myth, someone knows someone who has done a gall bladder flush to differing extremes. The excellent and invaluable "Healing with Whole Foods" by Paul Pitchford contains a thorough flush for the Gall Bladder. It is a short sharp detox and should be carried out under the guidance of a health professional. A simplified version would be to increase the intake of green apples in your diet. Try fasting for a day eating only apples and drinking warm lemon water. Apples are great for cooling for the system and are excellent at softening hardened masses within the body such as gall stones. They are high in pectin which cleanse toxins from the digestive system. All making it easier for the liver to handle any heated overload.

Traditionally Spring is the time for fasting. Christians have Lent, Muslims have Ramadan and in Chinese Medicine this season is used for a good physical clear out. Choose a month in Spring to detox by consciously eating less dairy, meat and processed carbohydrates. I like February because it's short. Make an effort to eat more seeds and nuts. Use only olive oil and sunflower oil to cook with and try to steam or bake most foods. Drink a cup of hot water and lemon first thing in the morning and eat two radishes between meals. Eat at least four portions of oily fish such as mackerel or herring every week, if not eating the fish, take two teaspoons of flax oil either poured over grains or vegetables or directly off the spoon. Keep food simple and fresh to unload the system. Detoxing isn't about punishing the body it's about being good to yourself and increasing vitality. Embody the flexibility of the liver/gall bladder do what you can, do what you want. Any one of the above will have a positive effect on the body. Your attitude and motivation is just as important as what you do.

Wake up Juice

1 large carrot
2 stalks of celery
or 1/4 bulb of celeriac
1 large handful of flat leaf parsley, spinach or watercress
1 lemon
1 red apple

A variety of enzymes are produced by our body and are present in food. However cooking kills food enzymes instantly. So juices are a great way to get plenty of food enzymes into our system. Chinese medicine does not recommend raw food alone as a healthy diet especially if our constitution is cold, weak or frail. Raw food will only further weaken the system. However with a balanced constitution raw food in some form is recommended daily. Ideally the juices should also contain the fibre from the fruit or vegetable to further aid digestion. This recipe is very palatable and appealing to the eye. The Celery is full of magnesium and flat leaf parsley full of vitamin C and Chloropyhll to stimulate the flow of bile whilst the lemon activates liver enzyme release. This is your morning shot of super energy.

Tapanade

This is a great spread to have in the fridge. Its great tossed through pasta, it makes a great stuffing for meat and really brightens up any sandwich or wrap. It is Mediterranean in origin, I have adapted the recipe by adding sunflower seeds to give it some crunch and bite whilst at the same time providing omega-3 and omega-6 essential fatty acids. The sour flavour of the olives help to increase the production of bile which helps to break down fats.

50–200g pitted green olives
75g sundried tomatoes
2 cloves garlic
3 tbls olive oil
Handful of chives
2 handfuls of flat leaf parsley
100g sunflower seeds
2 tbsp capers

It is possible to smash and chop all the ingredients by hand but for speedy easy put them in a blender and whiz until you have the desired texture.

Simple Salads

Any fresh vegetable will work in a salad. Keep it small, simple and uncooked and your liver will thank you for it. In many Mediterranean countries small plates of salad are served before the main meal. They freshen the palate and aid the digestion. So instead of the dependable meat and two veg, mix it up a little. Here are a few suggestions;

- **5 Grated carrots and a large handful of chopped coriander/ parsley**
- **½ Grated Celeriac and ½ tangy apple**
- **5 Grated Carrots and ½ grated daikon or 10 finely sliced radishes**
- **½ shredded white cabbage, finely sliced red onion, 4 grated carrots**
- **Thinly sliced fennel, yellow peppers**

Simple Dressing

With this dressing you can be creative. You can add fresh herbs, finely chopped garlic or toasted seeds. You can add mustard and/ or capers which is great over cooked vegetables. Add honey if your vegetables such as fennel like a little sweetness. To make the dressing Asian in flavour substitute mirin and rice vinegar for the lemon, sesame oil for sunflower oil and soy sauce for salt. Check in with your body and your cupboards. Express yourself and be creative.

Juice of 1 lemon or
2 tbsp of white wine vinegar
5 tbsp sunflower oil
Ground Black Pepper
Salt

Specific Liver/Gall Bladder Points

Gall Bladder 40 — impatience.
On the outside of the foot, in the hollow under your ankle bone. It encourages the stream of energy throughout the meridian and also encourages movement of liver energy. So by stimulating this point, rather than feeling like you are paddling upstream to where you want to go, you will glide effortlessly downstream with your river finding ways around obstacles and go with your flow.

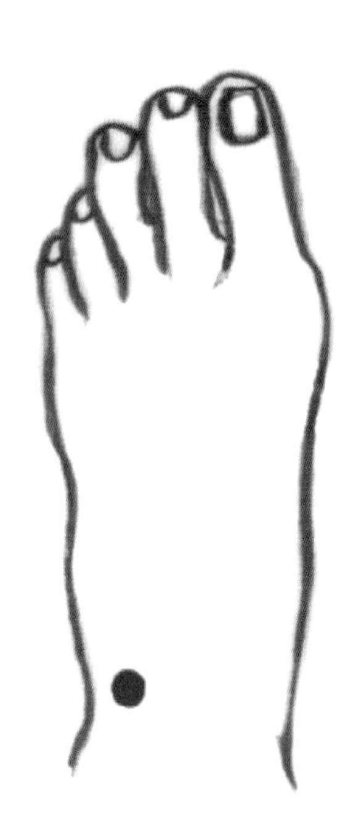

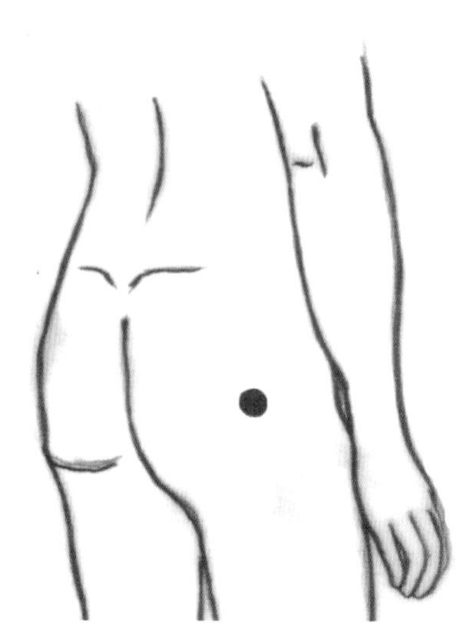

Gall Bladder 30 — stress.
The dint in your bum at the side, usually where the pocket of jean covers. Often we hold tension in our buttocks which can lead to lower back pain and exacerbate sciatica. Massaging all around this area and especially the point itself, can remove energetic blockage and relieve pain.

Specific Liver/Gall Bladder Points

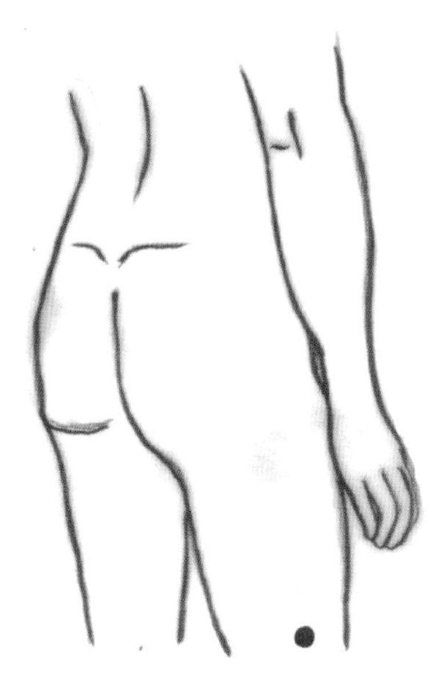

Gall Bladder 31 — flexibility.
With your arms by your sides, press into the point where the middle finger lands on the outside midline of the leg. To do this effectively, put your feet together and raise the opposite arm over your head so that the fingers sliding down your leg can reach the spot more easily. This yoga pose is called the standing wheel. Pressing and holding this point can clear hearing problems and help to free the mind, meaning you are more flexible physically and emotionally.

Liver 2 — irritable or angry at others.
The fleshy web between big toe and second toe is a good point to massage if you are suffering a build up of heat and anger. Press on this point and hold to relieve the hot headed feeling of frustration.

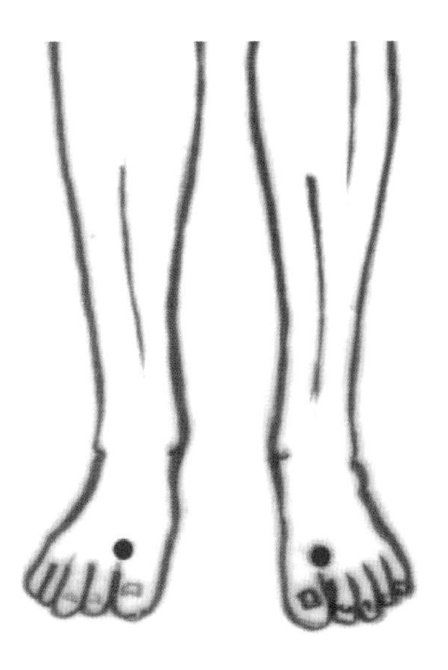

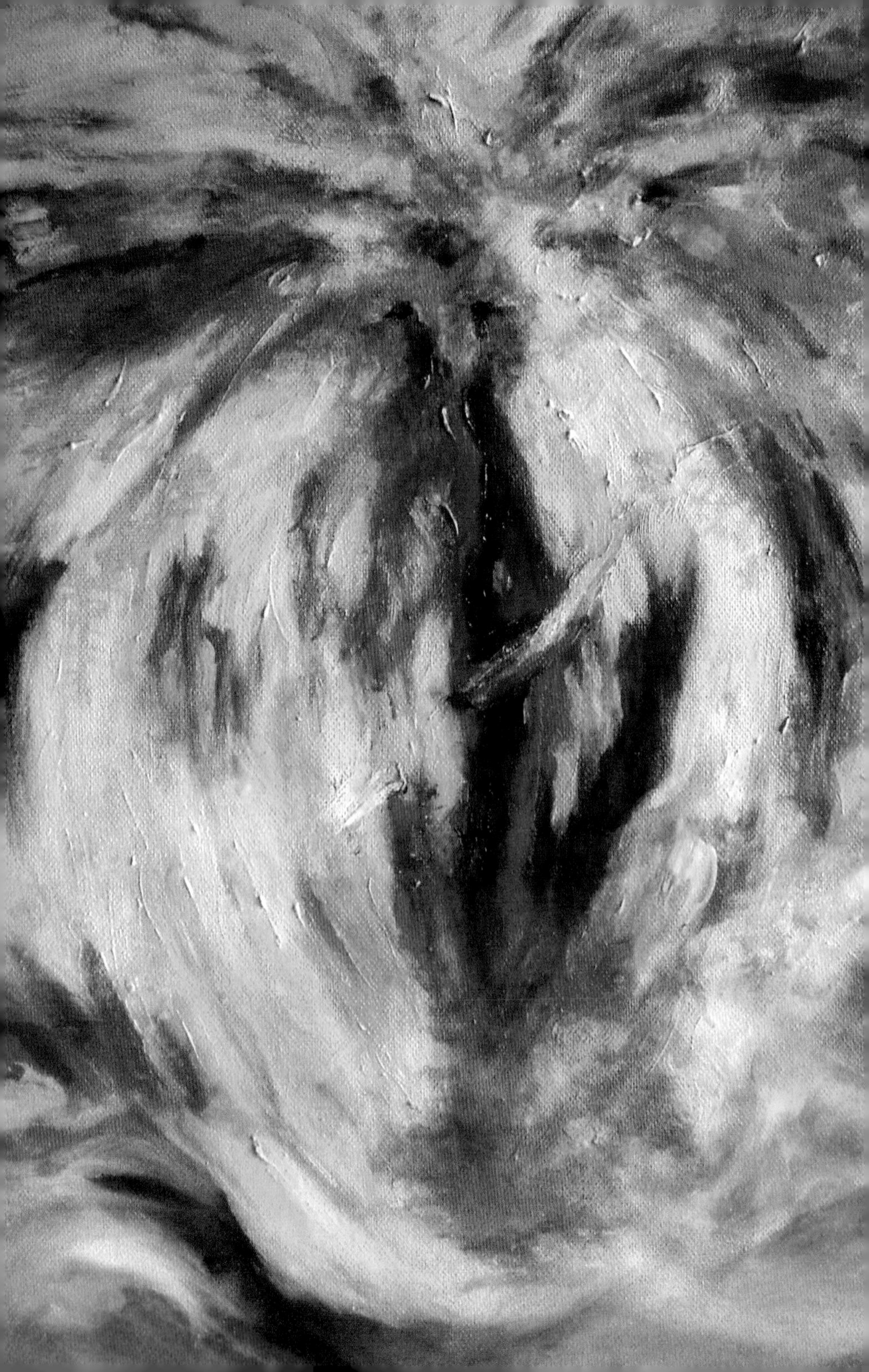

Chapter 5: Heart and Small Intestine

flavour	bitter
season	high summer
meridians & organs	heart & small intestine
properties	expansion
emotion	joy
colour	red

Overview

There is a difference in myself when I stop what I am doing, stop thinking and listen to the sounds around me without trying to work out what they are. I am not concerned with getting anything right, getting anything finished or getting anything. This non doing is the heart space, we are not worried about the future or reliving the past – we are in the present, we are in the heart.

Our natural state is joyous and happy; unfortunately we forget this as it becomes clouded by worries of the future and regrets of the past. However they are all just stories which we can drop, carry the wisdom, stop the record and live from the heart.

Which brings us to love, the emotion of the heart. To be in love is to be in the heart, to be in the present moment without judgement, to be joyous, open and happy. We may expect another can give us that feeling of being in love but really in truth it is all our own doing. It's a state of being which comes from nothing external. I remember watching squirrels jumping about on a wall on drizzly New Years day and I knew I was in love. I had no partner I was alone but I was totally in love and I am today, June 1st, the weather is different, the air is different, the kids are bouncing off the sofa, I am with a man with big arms and soft lips. I am still *in* love. That isn't to say that I may be both sad and smitten on other days. It's possible to be sad and still to be in love. You are in your body, at your very heart and in this place we know everything is as it should be and ultimately everything will be OK. For me that heart place is the kingdom of heaven within. It is where I know divine magic. At the intense points in my life such as my fathers death or when relationships end, in those places of deep grief where the world stops, I still felt truly comforted through my tears. I was still *in* love.

So what is the best way to get to this heart space? In our faced paced modern world we are often in the head, working things out, planning ahead or replaying situations, to try and figure things out. But to get to the heart space just requires a little time out from that; with a little less conversation; a little more being.

The best way I have found to support the body and mind is through meditation. Just like the physical muscle of the heart needs to be exercised so too does the emotional muscle through meditation practice. So focus on breathing, let the thoughts go, be in a different space for just five minutes and trust that will give a different perspective, one that comes from heart space rather than head space. A simple way to link the heart to food is to use speech and simply say thank you for the food on our plates, gratitude for the person it makes us into and the life it sustains. In this way we are *in* love with ourselves, accepting all of nature's bounty.

Food and drink can also support the travelling from head space to heart space. Our spirit/shen is said to be housed in the blood which the heart gives vibrancy. If we can keep our blood healthy and flowing evenly, external interactions and reactions will be grounded and come from the heart space of love. Out of balance we may be easily agitated, often running over situations over and over again in our mind to come up with solutions. This physically can lead to chest pain, sleeplessness and agitation. The mind may become confused and we may find it difficult to settle.

The acceptance of divine bounty touches briefly on the role of the small intestine. The heart when at peace radiates outwards and in keeping with yin/yang must therefore be able to receive. It is the role of the small intestine to filter emotional experiences and physical nourishment so presenting what is needed to the heart. What is not needed is passed on for excretion. In Chinese Medicine all organs are in-service to the heart keeping it balanced, open and joyous at the very seat of our soul.

There are some specific foods for the heart but really the heart is like a king/queen on a throne supported and protected by all his/her subjects, the organs. Food, drink and air are all taken in and transformed into blood, chi or waste by all the other organs in the body. However the heart just is, it plays no role in transformation or elimination. But it's not just a pump to enable transportation; it adds vibrancy to the blood and in doing so provides a stable home for the body-mind, enabling the experience of love and joy in life. So I decided to write recipes from the heart. Often their primary benefit from a Chinese Medicine point of view will be to other organs but ultimately they will bring health and happiness to the heart.

Foods at a Glance for Heart & Small Intestine

Lettuce, Chicory, Watercress
Mung Bean
Fresh Wheat Bread
Tomatoes
Coconut
Oats
Beetroot/Parsley
Basmati Rice
Fresh herbs such as Sage, Basil, Tarragon & Majoram

Heart Meditation

Sometimes when I sit on my cushion... actually sometimes I do anything except sit on my cushion, the washing up, phone calls to the bank, hoovering, writing this book, amazing the amount of distractions I find, to stop myself from just being, being in my body; focusing on my breathing, letting all thoughts go. But when I do I find my cushion, the muscles in my torso soften and the mid space in my chest opens.

When I get off the cushion I still have problems – frustration with the bank, exasperation with my children, anger with people who don't indicate on roundabouts. Problems don't necessarily go away because I meditate but they can have less of a mental, emotional and physical effect. This softening of the heart space in meditation can reduce stress and anxiety; therefore bring down blood pressure and lower cholesterol levels. You allow the emotion but realize it's not who you are and it, like everything, will pass. The emotions of anger, frustration, jealousy don't have to control the person you are and the choices you make. They can pass like clouds.

So just sit, there's no getting it right or wrong and there is no end, there is no goal. It's a practice and so impossible to get wrong.

Sit in a comfortable position whether it be on the floor cross legged, on a stool or on a chair, it doesn't matter. It is preferable to have a straight back, as if all the bones in your spine are a stack of golden pennies swaying, balancing and completely upright. Rest your hands comfortably on your knees. If it helps to travel inwards, begin the practice with the eyes shut. Once the mind has calmed a little and you have become completely present in the body in which you are sitting, open your eyes, letting your gaze fall gently downwards, a couple of feet in front of you. Just as in the Yin/Yang meditation don't focus on anything in particular, allow the gaze to be all encompassing as you are seeing all rather than looking at anything in particular. Allow the mouth to fall open slightly, relaxing the jaw and cheeks. Now just breathe. If you find the mind wandering to what colour you are going to paint the living room or to the argument you just had with your neighbour, let it go. Come back to the breath and allow the mind to rest. Think all the thoughts you are going to think when you get off the cushion or chair. If it helps, set a timer so that just for five minutes, or however long you want to sit, you can allow your thoughts to dissolve and the confidence in your natural dignity and beauty to shine through.

"We can learn how to develop a gentle but unshakeable composure. Our confidence in ourselves grows, and becomes so much greater that goodness and compassion begin naturally to radiate out from us and bring joy to others." ***The Tibetan Book of Living and Dying — Sogyal Rinpoche***

Summer Salad

Early summer of June and July is the time of the heart. The sunshine, on a good day fairly buzzes in the air and on your skin. The atmosphere is full of life and the garden is a riot of colour. Use this feast of colour to enrich our meals as we eat with our eyes, the sensory organ of the heart, not only our mouths. In these summer months we need to take light small meals and what better to make the heart sing than to prepare them with colour and care on your plate. Not all flowers are edible so do a reference check just to make sure what you are eating. Make sure you wash the flowers thoroughly and I wouldn't eat shop bought flowers as they are often sprayed with chemicals. The flowers in the recipe are really easy to grow in your garden or in a window box and they can be tossed through cooked rice, bulghar wheat or millet to add texture and vitality. Here I have chosen to toss them into a green leaf salad.

In Traditional Chinese Medicine the heart is the final place to add vibrancy to blood and it controls the flow and power of the blood around the body. In western medicine this would be covered by the rhythm of the heart, the contraction and expansion of the pericardium and the valves within the heart. They are kept regular and strong by the minerals calcium and magnesium.

Calendula petals
Violas (whole flowers)
Chive heads (whole flowers)
Nasturtium petals
Baby Spinach Leaves
Watercress or Rocket Leaves
Finely sliced radish
Finely shredded rainbow chard
Cherry Tomatoes

Leafy greens are a great source of calcium and magnesium, both of which keep blood flowing. Magnesium especially, is great at helping the body to relax and the blood vessels dilate.

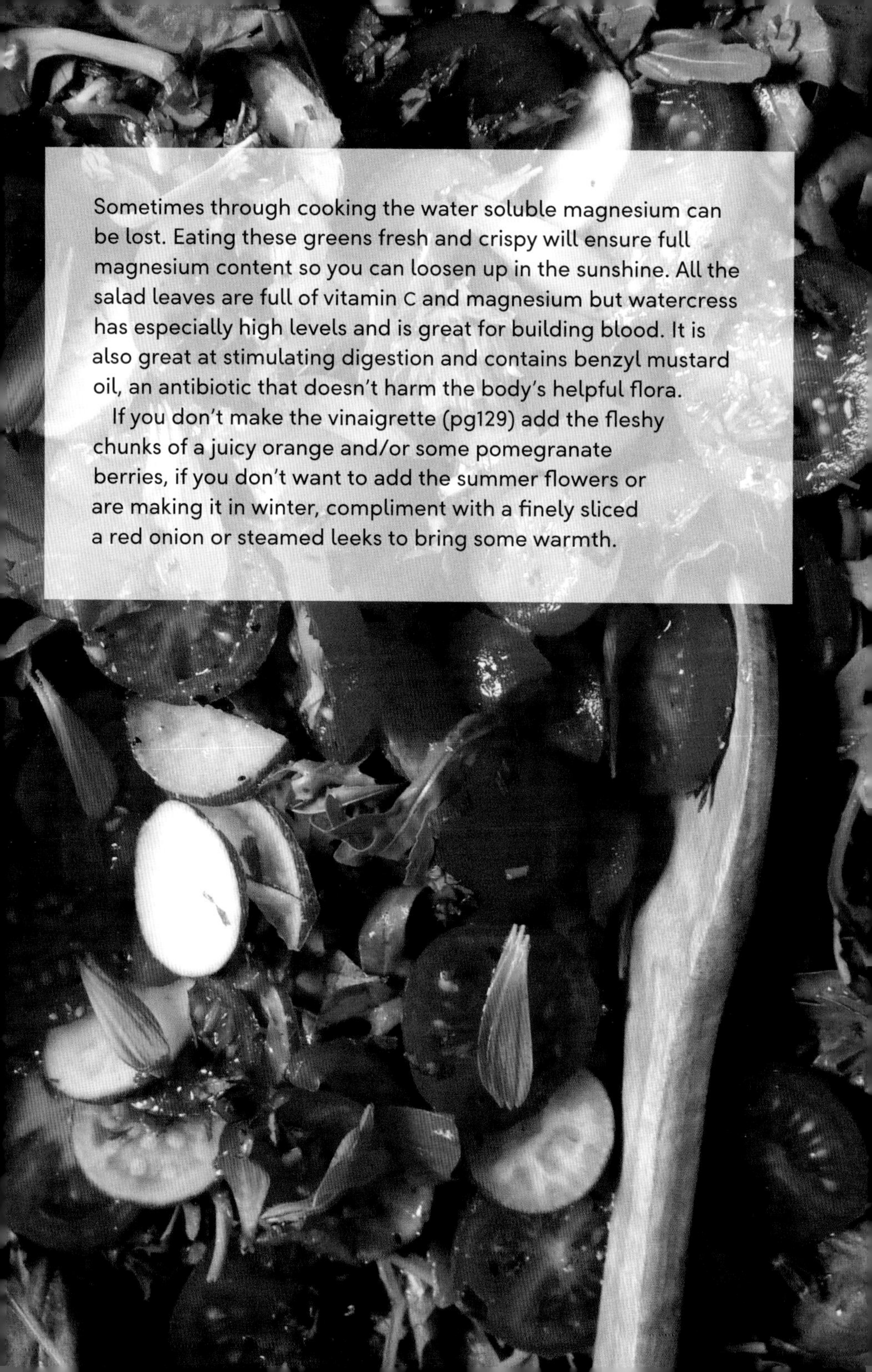

Sometimes through cooking the water soluble magnesium can be lost. Eating these greens fresh and crispy will ensure full magnesium content so you can loosen up in the sunshine. All the salad leaves are full of vitamin C and magnesium but watercress has especially high levels and is great for building blood. It is also great at stimulating digestion and contains benzyl mustard oil, an antibiotic that doesn't harm the body's helpful flora.

If you don't make the vinaigrette (pg129) add the fleshy chunks of a juicy orange and/or some pomegranate berries, if you don't want to add the summer flowers or are making it in winter, compliment with a finely sliced a red onion or steamed leeks to bring some warmth.

Tomato Sauce for Kids

As well as being full of vitamin C and other necessary vitamins and minerals tomatoes, peepers, potatoes and aubergines are part of the deadly nightshade family. They are an amazing food group as they support the yin restorative qualities within the body whilst encouraging expansion and movement. And we love'em, potatoes and tomatoes are huge cash crops in the western world. However too much yin is never a good thing. Take mashed potatoes for example, the ultimate comfort food; the yin which is receptive and compassionate soothes an overstressed body. But if they become our only food, it can induce a soporiphic laziness giving a heavy stodgy feeling. It should also be noted that some people can be sensitive to this food group for some it can aggravate conditions such as rheumatoid arthritis. To reduce sensitivity try cooking or roasting them as they are just too good to miss. But back to the recipe on page.

Unfortunately my kids only eat broccoli or they think they only eat broccoli. This and raw carrots is the only vegetable they allow on their plates. I have heard said that a child feels they only control what they put into them, what comes out of them and nothing in the world around them. I also feel that because food is my passion they are rebelling so I pick my battles and let them have that control over their plate. For me it means I have become adept at hiding vegetables in stews, soups and sauces. This tomato sauce is made every couple of weeks and used for meatballs, spaghetti Bolognese, pizzas and spread on their favourite after school snack, flat tortillas with melted cheese.

2 tablespoons of sunflower oil
1 large knob of butter
1 large onion, sliced
4 cloves of garlic, smashed
1 medium carrot, chopped
1 medium stick of

- celery, chopped
- Handful of fresh sage (half a handful if dried)
- 1 roasted sweet potato, sliced
- 1 tin of plum peeled tomatoes
- 250g passata
- Sprinkle of seaweed
- 1 tablespoon honey
- Salt and pepper to taste
- Vegetable stock if needed

Heat the oil and butter together, when hot fry the onions for a couple of minutes. Stirring occasionally, making sure they don't stick. Add the garlic, carrot, celery and sage turning down the heat to low and cover with a lid so that the vegetables all sweat together. After 10 minutes pop in the sweet potato, tinned tomatoes, seaweed and passata. Stir it all up and turn up the heat a little so that all the ingredients simmer together for at least 20 minutes. Take it off the heat and blitz with a stick blender whilst it's still in the pan. Be careful with splashes, its like molten lava if it hits your skin. Squeeze the honey in and let it blend with the flavours adding salt and pepper to taste. It will be quite a thick sauce, perfect for pizzas and baking fish in but you may want to add a little vegetable stock to thin it for spaghetti Bolognese or tomato soup.

Tomato Sauce for Kids

Pesto

Even though Basil has a sweet smell, just like the lettuce juice (pg 128) it has a bitter taste and it is that flavour that benefits the Heart and Small Intestine. At an emotional level it is bitterness that allows for love, without the pain which opens us, our love and life experience cannot expand. As the lyrical master Leonard Cohen says: ***"Forget your perfect offering. There is a crack, a crack in everything. That's how the light gets in."***

The heart is the place where we transform our life experience. If we build up a protective wall through fear or pain it can prevent us from really connecting, from empathy, understanding others and the world around us. So cultivate a softness, an openness, a vulnerability that is safe in the knowledge that you will always love yourself; giving your heart a house to experience the joy of life, with all its bittersweet love.

240g fresh Basil
Couple of handfuls of fresh baby spinach leaves or watercress
100g sunflower seeds or pine nuts
100g parmesan cheese
2 tablespoons olive oil

Who doesn't love pesto? Even my fussy kids shout hooray when its pesto pasta for tea. This is so easy and fresh. By adding spinach or watercress it's packed with vitamin C, Calcium and Magnesium. Simply put all the ingredients into a blender, pour over the olive oil and blitz. Feel free to substitute goat's cheese for the parmesan cheese, just add a little more as it tends to be milder in flavour. Toss the pesto through the warm pasta so that the water soluble minerals are not lost through cooking.

French Bean Salad

From a Chinese medicine point of view, French Green Beans are more typically a liver cleansing food but for two reasons I have included them here. Firstly they are at the height in the summer season and I think that vibrational atunement with what's in season where you live is important and secondly they make my heart sing. When I see this delicate elegant vegetable I always feel I am in for a treat.

There are many ways to eat them. Toss them with anchovies, mustard and soft new potatoes, add them to tuna and soft boiled eggs for nicoise, steam them and drizzle sesame oil and seeds – all light and delicious but here I have chosen very simply garlic, olive oil and good sea salt, the perfect accompaniment to a chilled glass of white wine in a sunny garden.

As many green beans as possible or if not 200g

3-4 tbsp good green olive oil

2-3 cloves of garlic

Chop the tiny stalks of the top but leave the tiny tails on. Steam them for between 4–8 minutes depending on the thickness of your bean. You don't want squeaky or soggy beans. Meanwhile squash and finely chop the garlic. Add it to the olive oil which has been warming on a medium heat and fry them gently you don't want them to burn just to exude the flavour into the oil. After a minute or so drizzle this garlic oil over the strained beans and crumble some large salt flakes over the top.

Beans and Rice

Beans and rice is a traditional African food which was taken by slaves and became popular all over the Americas. You can see why, it is relatively cheap, easy and quick to cook. All pulses are a great at controlling fat metabolism and their high dietary fibre assist cholesterol in leaving the body. The basmati rice has a delicate fragrance which is said to lift the heart whilst the Mung Beans are especially recommended for their ability to cleanse the arteries. Beans and rice when taken together become a complete protein so they are a great food combination. Taken with a few vegetables, perhaps some raw salads from the Liver chapter. It is the perfect meal containing all vitamins and minerals without overloading the system with too many flavours.

100g Pre soaked mung beans
100g Basmati Rice
Enough water or stock to cover and up to the 2nd knuckle of your index finger
Sprinkle of Wakame seaweed

Place all the ingredients into a saucepan with a good fitting lid. Bring to the boil then immediately turn the heat as low as it will to for ten to fifteen minutes, leaving the lid on. If after the this time not all the water has been absorbed cook with the lid off for a few minutes. Never stir the rice use a fork to prize it from the sides. When cooking beans and rice together I salt at the end of cooking as salt during cooking can make the skin of beans tough. Adding seaweed whilst cooking however will soften beans and make them easier to digest.

Stuffed Tomatoes and Peppers

By building blood and ensuring its smooth transportation through clear arteries we ensure the heart is healthy. The clarity and peace this gives the body mind cannot be bought or grasped by attaining anything external it must be generated internally. Red peppers and tomatoes are full of biovlaviniols and vitamin C which as powerful antioxidants are great for clearing arteries and aiding strong, flexible capillary walls. Bioflavinols ensure the blood doesn't become too sticky and its presence is essential for Vitamin C to be effective. We all know how effective Vitamin C is for protecting against colds and flu but its importance in healthy blood is often overlooked. It helps excrete cholesterol and is required for brain chemicals which affect mood. Iron which builds blood needs vitamin C to be present for its absorption. So for a stress free happy heart try eating plenty of purple and red fruits and vegetables together with of course those green leafy herbs and vegetables.

250g uncooked basmati rice
6 red peppers
6 large tomatoes
3-4 tbsp Pesto (pg 121)
50g parmesan cheese
2-3 balls of Mozzarella cheese

Cook the rice as directed on the packet. It doesn't have to be basmati but the delicate fragrance of basmati is said to enter and benefit the heart meridian. Wash the tomatoes and peppers and slice the tops of them so that they can still stand upright on a baking tray. Scoop out the insides of the pepper and discard. If you want you can add the innards of the tomatoes to the rice mixture but it will make it wetter and take longer to cook. Combine together the cooked rice, pesto and parmesan and fill the tomatoes and peppers with the mixture. The amount of rice required will vary as do the size of peppers. Slice the mozzarella 2-3 mm thick and place like a hat on top of the stuffed pepper or tomato. Place on a baking tray and roast for 45 in a preheated oven at 180.

African Coco Curry

I cook this meal at many of my catering events and am indebted to the World Café Cookbook. It's a real show stopper with its unusual mix of flavours. Most people are used to Indian curry with cumin and coriander or Thai with its use of coconut milk and chilli flakes but this is something new; fresh yet warming and comforting. A luxurious curry that will, with its sweet flavour, nourish the body and with the beans, rice and coconut milk cleanse and nourish the blood.

1 tbsp butter & 1 tbsp sunflower oil
2 medium onions
5 cloves garlic
3 inches fresh ginger
2 sweet potatoes
4 carrots
80/120g fresh parsley
Large sprig of fresh thyme
500 ml stock
1 tin of coconut milk
1 tin of cannellini beans
1 pre roasted butternut squash

Spice mix

10 curry leaves
1 tsp ground cinnamon
1 tsp tumeric
1 tsp ground black pepper
1 tsp all spice
Strong pinch of chilli flakes and cayenne pepper
Salt and pepper

Melt the butter and oil together and fry the onions, when they are soft, add the ginger, garlic and spice mix. Stir and fry these together for about 2-5 minutes then toss in the cubed carrot and sweet potato, stirring for another couple of minutes. If you haven't pre roasted the butternut squash you can add it here. However roasting the squash in its skin adds great texture right at the end when the sweet potato has probably dissolved into the coconut milk. Cover the vegetables with stock, bring to the boil and simmer for about twenty minutes until the carrots are almost soft, add in the thyme, most of the chopped fresh parsley, the coconut milk and cannellini beans. Cook for a further ten minutes ensuring that the coconut milk doesn't boil and just before the end add the roasted butternut squash, the remaining chopped parsley and heat through.

Lettuce Juice

As discussed in other recipes, green leaves are full of chlorophyll which helps clear the liver and vitamin C which helps detox the blood. However lettuce has an extra soporiphic quality. If you think back to the tale of the flopsy bunnies by Beatrix Potter, the bunnies ate lots of lettuce and fell asleep and that's how Mr. McGregor could catch them in his bag. It contains the sedative lactucarium which will relax the nerves and so aid sleep.

2 or 3 heads of lettuce especially the outer green leaves should be juiced and the liquor can be kept in a small bottle in the fridge for a couple of days. Two tablespoons one hour before bedtime will help the body relax and enter sleep. Watercress could also be added, its high potassium levels can also prevent insomnia. All these properties help to build the blood and it is in the blood which our shen, our consciousness resides. If we don't house the spirit it can become confused and agitated, leading to palpitations, anxiety, insomnia and restlessness. Once grounded, the shen allows us to connect to the world from a vibrant, clear centre. We know from our bodies wisdom that peace love and contentment come from within.

Beetroot & Horseradish Relish

Combining beetroot with horseradish has been a revelation in flavour and I put it in sandwiches and wraps if I don't have time to make the full salad. It has reintroduced me to delicious beetroot. Forget the memory of the jars of mini blood balls with no flavour save that of malt vinegar. Beetroot is great for the blood, maintaining strong veins, arteries and capillaries. Parsley is a mild diuretic and is full of vitamin C, way more than citrus fruit and so a great antioxidant; All together this salad is perfect for the heart and a summer barbeque.

4 cooked beetroot
1 onion
Large handful fresh parsley
2 tbsp horseradish sauce (or 3 if fresh plus 2 tblsp cider vinegar)
2 tsp honey
Salt to taste (not much if you've used the horseradish)

Grate the beetroot and chop the onion finely. mix together with the chopped parsely, horseradish, vinegar, honey and salt. Let it sit and blend for an hour before serving.

Orange Vinaigrette

This is a perfect summer vinaigrette with just the amount of sweetness and zing to balance out the bitter flavours of a green leaf salad. This vinaigrette shouldn't be limited to just salads though it's really good over broccoli or other green vegetables.

120 ml orange juice
60 ml red wine vinegar
90 ml olive oil
2 tsp maple syrup
2 tsp Dijon mustard
2 tbls Tarragon or coriander

Put or pour all the ingredients into a screw top jar and shake vigorously for a couple of minutes, toss softly through your salad.

Specific Heart/Small Intestine Points

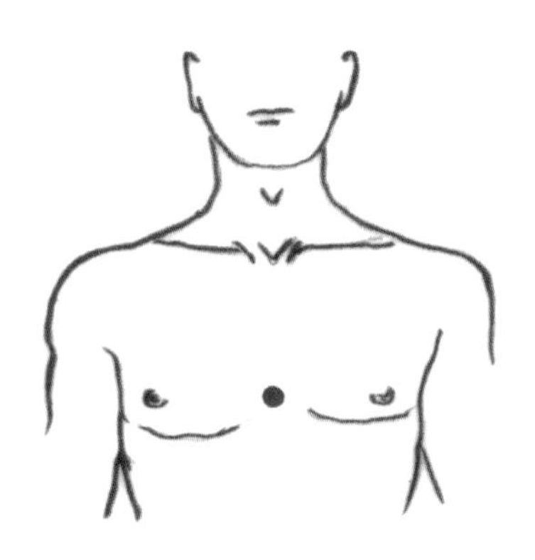

CV 17 — well being.
Midway down the breastbone find the hollow big enough for a digit to sink into. It relaxes the muscles around the heart and chest, so great before a stressful meeting or sitting down to meditate. It can really bring us back into our bodies, making our shoulders drop from our ears and allow our breath to sink into our bellies.

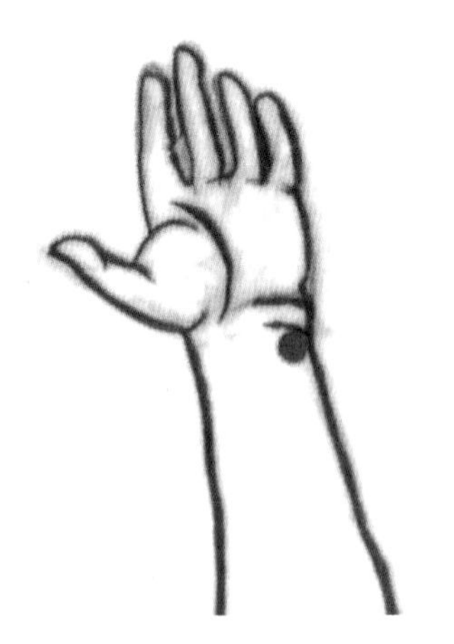

Heart 7 — being calm, being present.
The crease of your wrist under the little finger. This is a strong point on the heart channel and will steady not sedate the heart. I would recommend taking seven deep breaths, holding each one at the end of the out breath to really calm the spirit and bring us back into our unshakable selves.

Specific Heart/Small Intestine Points

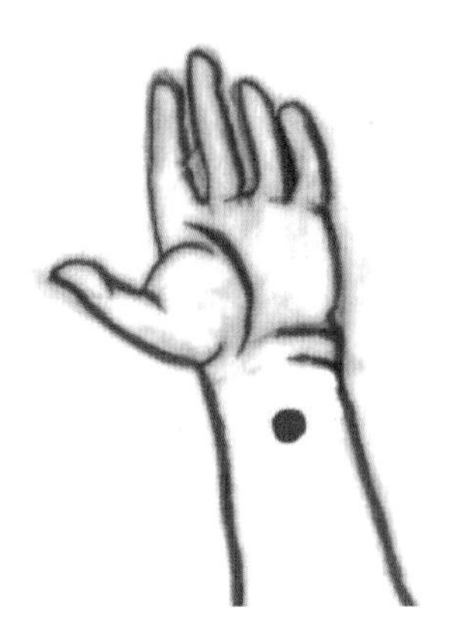

Heart Protector 6 — balance in an unsteady world.
Three fingers up from the crease at your wrist on the inner mid line. This point regulates Heart Chi and blood. It relaxes the diaphragm and calms the stomach. So a great point for nausea, sea sickness and vomiting.

Spleen 6 — building and moving blood.
4 fingers up from the ankle bone on the inside mid line. This is a very versatile point because the Spleen, Kidney and Liver Meridians cross at that point, so press or rub the whole area to regulate, invigorate, build blood strength and release tension in the abdomen.

Chapter 6: Stomach and Spleen

flavour	sweet
season	late summer
meridians & organs	stomach & spleen
properties	centering & supporting
emotion	satisfaction, mothering
colour	orange

Overview

In Chinese Medicine there is an extra added season, late summer. The time when the heat and buzz of summer has died down; flowers have turned to fruits ready for harvesting. It's a time of comfort and support, some say the most important energetic time for our bodies. If we can't openly receive this abundance then what is life, but a struggle. It's the same with food. No matter how much broccoli we eat, if we cannot receive its nutrients it can be no more nutritious than chewing cardboard. Food is life and our relationship to food therefore mirrors our connection to life. Is our relationship healthy, life giving and joyous or is it controlling and dysfunctional? Stomach/spleen is an essential place to start to love life, to love food and to love ourselves.

So to begin at the beginning, food and its digestion does not start when food hits the stomach, it begins as we think about food — those digestive juices start flowing as desire begins to take a form... Hmmmmn, what shall I eat? The food is placed in the mouth (an important part of digestion often overlooked) and chew, chew, chew, this releases the saliva which begins the first breakdown process. Then onto the stomach, very acidic, more breakdown of the food which is sent onto the spleen where the nutrients are taken up and dispersed into the body. This fits easily with the western model of digestion, only in Chinese Medicine, the spleen takes the chi from the food and together with the small intestine and lung transforms it into blood and our unique energy or chi. East or West it doesn't matter, the important word here is uptake. It gives a really good sense as to the healthy energy of these organs. It's like studying or reading this book. It began in the mind to get the book and read it, you are taking in the words. Some of the ideas you might keep, some of the recipes may become part of your everyday life. Other ideas and foods maybe stored away to bring out later and some of the information may mean nothing to you and will be forgotten. *Your experience of this book will be unique, as is your digestion and uptake of nutrition and the transformation to energy.* It relies on far more than just the mechanical functioning of organs and the chemical content of the food; for the stomach and spleen it can all be very emotional.

So how to enhance uptake and receive nature's bounty? Firstly the body needs to feel supported, physically and emotionally. Remember a time when you last had a hug, a really good hug that you relaxed into. That's the support the stomach and spleen is looking for. A big comforting hug, which it gets through sweet flavoured food. This could be why often chocolate is seen as a comfort food. I know when I first became a mother I craved chocolate and Ice-cream, preferably chocolate ice cream. Physically my energy was stretched and emotionally I needed support. I find in my Shiatsu practice that these are the organs and meridians where emotional needs can be confused with physical desires; that we sometimes use food to meet an emotional need. As I've said before there is nothing wrong with eating chocolate. But if it is emotional support you are looking for a chocolate bar can't love you and may even create a vicious circle of depleted energy and therefore increased sugar cravings. Often unresolved emotional issues can create a deep hunger causing a cycle of addiction to mask the pain. So whilst the recipes here will give the body sweet fulfilment, use them consciously to maintain the bodies natural balance and go get a hug, a massage, find a good councillor, go dancing, go to the beach, get some sleep, talk to someone who will listen. It's about being good to ourselves, loving ourselves and food is only a part of that.

Chinese medicine links this season, these organs and meridians to the mother, which is usually our first experience of nourishment and care. How we received care as babies and young children is often the pattern set up as to how we care for ourselves. No matter how positive or negative that relationship may have been ultimately we must learn to parent ourselves and find our own internal mother who nurtures and cares for us. In the soft space of care we can truly receive what is given to us; through food, through sunlight, through laughter, through children, through kisses, through grief, through beauty, through life, through love.

Foods at a glance for Stomach & Spleen

Grains – millet, brown rice and buckwheat & quinoa

Root vegetables – carrot, parsnip, sweet potato

Orange vegetables, squash and pumpkin

Lentils especially the orange ones

Fennel including the seed

Peas

Be careful not to flood the food with fluid

Well & slow cooked food

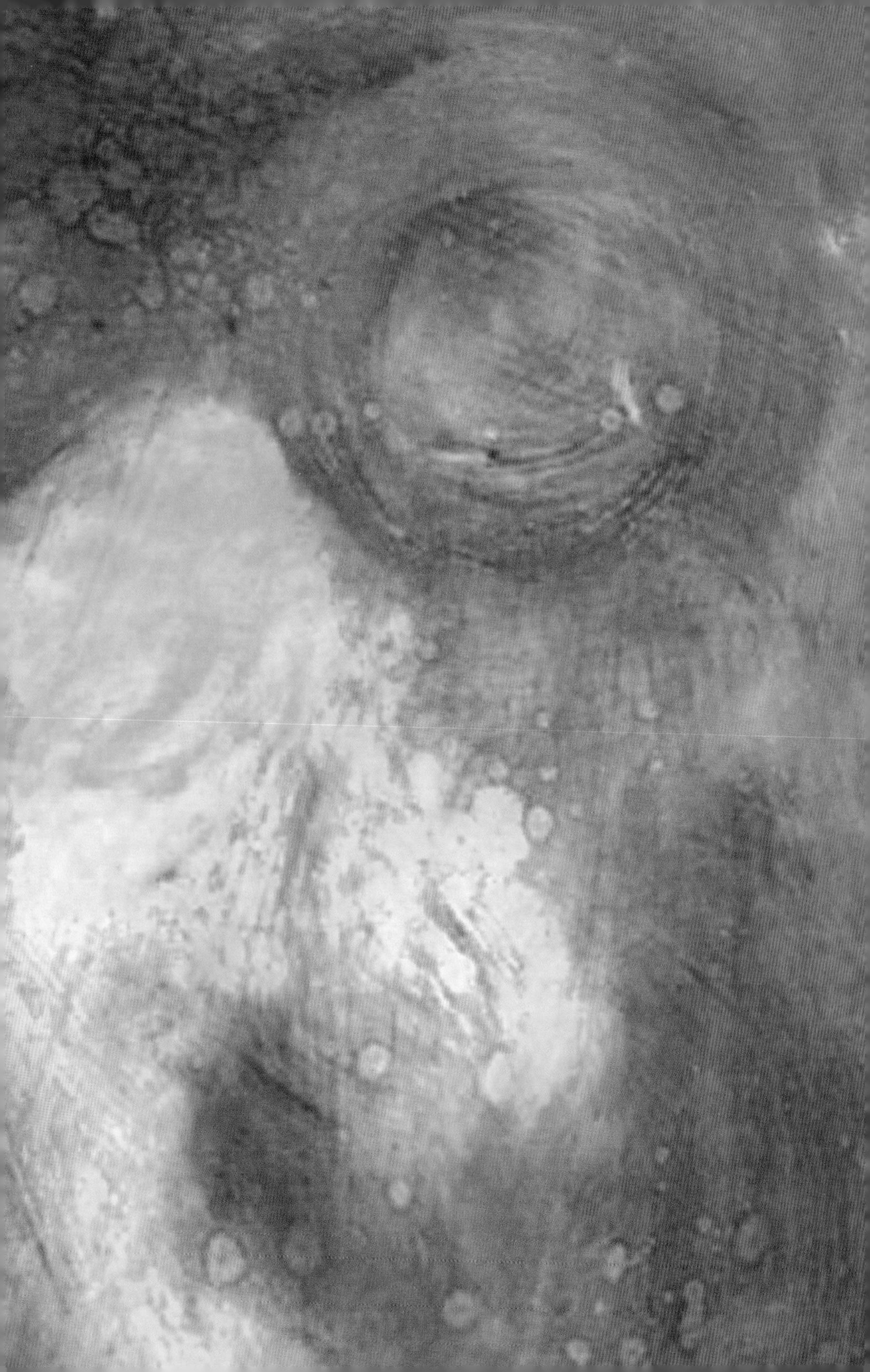

Spleen Meditation

Our ultimate mother is the earth. It benevolently gives us everything we need. Use this meditation to connect with the earth and increase your abundance, becoming open to receive all it has to offer.

Find somewhere to sit where you are comfortable and supported. It can be on a couch, a straight backed chair, a bed leaning your back against the headboard or the floor and use the wall.

Close your eyes and relax, let your shoulders drop and feel your hips connecting with whatever it is they are sitting on. Take a few deep breaths, imagine whatever is supporting your back is a great big tree. Its trunk is broad and strong. The earth beneath you is warm, the grass soft like a downy carpet. Lean back against the tree, feel its support, take your mind's eye and look up into its branches as it dapples the filtered sunlight with its leaves. Now come back and sit under the tree, facing straight ahead. As you breathe in, imagine energy coming up directly from the earth, into your legs and hips, filling your body all the way up and leaving through the top of your head as you breathe out. On the out breath, leaves fall gently to the ground bringing your attention to the earth as you breathe in once more. You are creating a cycle. Do this for as long as you need to. Feel your tree holding you, protecting you. The earth is supporting you and the falling leaves are bringing you everything you desire, as easily and effortlessly as breathing.

Oven Roasted Vegetables

It seems kind of funny to be including a recipe for a very simple dish of vegetables that are slow roasted in the oven. They almost need no recipe, all they are is all we need, no fancy sauce, no lengthy preparation simply wash, sometimes peel and stick in the oven. The sweetness that happens when vegetables are slow roasted is fantastic and so comforting especially when served with the herby millet (pg 151).

I know if you are on weight watchers or other calorie controlled diets you can be discouraged from eating naturally sweet vegetables but food is about more than just the calories it contains. Think of the ways we link food to the mind — "eating of words", "food for thought" or "verbal diarrhoea". Often in stressfull situations such as exams, worries about family members or completion of an important project we may crave chocolate or sweet foods as the mind overworks and "chews over ideas" or the stomach becomes knotted with worries. Use sweet tasting food to bring a feeling of support and understanding, emotionally and physically. Rather than denying ourselves and sending signals that our desires are wrong. Calm and support your mind by choosing these sweet foods that help you receive the bounty of the earth.

Sweet Potato
Parsnip
Butternut Squash
Beetroot
Onions
Carrot

Sweet potato can be roasted with its skin on simply prick with a sharp knife so it doesn't explode in the oven. Roast it at about 180 for 45-60 mins. Then slit it in half and fork through the contents. Another way to roast this potato is to peel them and cut them into chunky wedges. Roast in a mix of sunflower and olive oil for 45 mins. Turn and baste them once during this time so they get a lovely caramel colour. Butternut squash can be peeled and chopped into slightly smaller wedges and cooked at the same time as the sweet potato. The bulbous base of the butternut I usually scoop out the seeds but don't bother peeling. It can be really fiddley for a small amount of squash return. If you have any of these roasted vegetables left over keep them in the fridge and add them to a tomato sauce later in the week. The carrots take slightly longer than the butternut squash and so should be sliced slightly thinner and the parsnips I take out the fibrous inner core before roasting and chop the same size as the butternut squash.

Beetroot I pierce and wrap in tin foil. After roasting for about an hour their skins should rub off using the tin foil.

Onions can be roasted many ways.You can leave them in their skin to be squeezed out after an hour in the oven but generally I cook them by taking off their skins, quartering them, leaving the roots on and sprinkling them throughout the other vegetables in the roasting dish.

Quinoa, Courgette & Carrot Salad

This is a great dish to eat if the body is feeling a bit sluggish and floppy. The orange juice, zest and coriander get the taste buds zinging whilst keeping things sweet. Whilst the flavours of this salad are delicate and light, the raw carrot, courgette and quinoa are solid and substantial. It's impossible to eat this salad without chewing which I know sounds obvious but all too often with a fast paced life our food is consumed quickly, on the run or in the car. If we don't chew our food, we skip this early, essential stage of digestion, the carbohydrates are not transformed into sugars and so give us an unsatisfied feeling after eating. This dish needs chewing, all the ingredients taste sweet to the palate, reducing cravings and ensuring a slow release of energy to the body.

2 Carrots
1 Courgette
100g Quinoa
60g fresh coriander
1 pomegranate
1 tbsp pumpkin seeds
1 tbsp poppy seeds
1 orange, juice and zest

Cover the quinoa with water, bring to the boil and simmer for approx. 20 minutes. When cooked the quinoa look like they are kind of individual spirals with little tails, cute food! Strain and rinse the quinoa and leave to cool while you grate the carrots, the courgette and chop the coriander. Cut the pomegranate in half, bashing the back with a wooden spoon and squeezing out the bright red juicy berries, making sure none of the bitter pith makes its way in. When complete, combine all the ingredients in a bowl and chew. This is great on its own but is really good with a pan fried duck breast.

Light Leek and Potato Soup

Lentil and potato soup seems like quite a heavy dish for the summer but this adaptation of a Davrick Leggit recipe includes lemon and mint which makes it very light and perfect for a comforting supper on an August evening. The small orange lentils really take no time at all to cook and are perfect at supporting the stomach and spleen. In fact they will also benefit the large intestine and the heart/small intestine because of their high dietary fibre. The leeks add a sweetness so if you are craving sugar, sugar, sugar, try cooking any of the onion family, taste their sweetness and be assured of their nourishment.

The stomach and spleen being responsible for the emotional support of the system but it also has a physical support. The spleen is in control of general muscle tone. If stomach/spleen energy is strong, the body remains toned but if it is weakened then muscle tone and organs can only be upheld through exercise or in extreme cases surgery. So prevent prolapse and try this soup! It's warm heartiness will support the body physically and emotionally.

2 large leeks
1 table sp olive oil
Knob of butter
½ pound red lentils
3 potatoes
2 pints stock
2 bay leaves
2 tsp fresh mint
1-2 lemons
Salt and freshly ground black pepper to taste

Heat the oil and butter, add the leeks and sweat them on a medium heat for 5-10 minutes until they are soft and slightly translucent. Keep the lid on so that all the juices are collected

in the pan. Toss in the washed red lentils, bay leaf and cubed peeled potatoes. Stir them in the juicy leeks and leave to sweat for a couple more minutes. Stir again ensuring the lentils have absorbed the juices but not stuck to the pan, now add the stock. I use miso in most of the recipes but any good quality vegetable or chicken stock is fine. Bring it to the boil, keep stirring every so often because the red lentils can have a tendency to stick, then simmer for about 20 minutes until the potatoes are just beginning to break up and the lentils have disintegrated.
At this point take it off the heat and stir in the lemon juice and the finely chopped mint. Add the finely chopped mint and half the lemon juice, taste as you stir, you don't want to overpower the other subtle flavours, now you are good to go.

Speedy Peachy Rice Pudding

Normally my recipes are quick and require little fuss in the kitchen. This one isn't fussy but it does require patience and about 45 minutes of your time. It's an adaptation of a Jamie Oliver recipe and I like it because it tastes of luxury and decadence and yet its sweetness comes from a natural grain not from processed sugar. The Arborio rice works well because the dessert has some substance and needs chewing, even better for digestion and even more sweetness.

85g butter
2 vanilla pods
300g Arborio rice
1 litre full fat milk
6 ripe peaches (or mango)
1 tablespoon of Apple Concentrate
½ cinnamon stick
Zest and juice of orange

Melt the butter and add the seeds from the vanilla pod. Heat for a minute so the aroma begins to release but don't burn them. Add the Arborio rice and stir it into the butter for a couple of minutes until the butter is absorbed by the rice. Then add a ladle of milk, which is kept at just below boiling in another pan. Stir in this milk until it is absorbed and then add another, stir again until it is absorbed. Just like a normal risotto you have to stir all the time whilst adding the liquid ladle by ladle, as the risotto progresses you can add two ladles of milk at a time. It will take between 30 and 45 minutes for all the milk to be absorbed and for the rice to cook. You may need more milk than I have recommended and don't forget to stir vigorously as this action will start the process of breaking down the carbohydrates into sweet sugar.

The stewed peaches or mangos are a healthy replacement the dollop of jam that my mum used to add. Quarter the peaches and remove the stones. Although this can be done easier after they are cooked as the flesh is softer you need asbestos fingers; your choice either the flesh of the peach suffers or the flesh of your fingers. Place the peaches in a heavy based saucepan with the cinnamon stick, apple concentrate, orange juice and zest. Heat them slowly for 5-10 minutes so that they are oozy, juicy but still retain some firmness. Spoon the luxury onto the steaming, silky rice pud.

Butternut and Miso Soup

Late summer moving to autumn, the sun still shines but the air is chilly and the evenings creep closer. Pumpkins and squashes fill the shops, their vibrant warming colour containing all the energy of orange sunshine that went before. Their sweet flavour and orange colour mean they are perfect for the Stomach and Spleen. They are a highly alkaline food, aiding digestion and boosting the chi. Some western research shows they improve insulin levels and lower blood sugar which is in the realm of spleen/pancreas. Cooking the butternut squash with Kombu will help reduce swelling and edema in the body whilst the miso will strengthen the bladder/kidney and increase the probiotic flora in the large intestine. The thyme is an antispasmodic herb and together with the squash can reduce pain and stomach cramps. This is a great all round soup to harmonize and soothe digestion whilst supporting flow and movement of energy all round the body.

1 butternut squash
1 leek
Generous bunch of thyme
1 pack 340g soft tofu
1 tablespoon miso paste
Small strip of Kombu seaweed
Sea Salt or gomasio to taste

Peel and deseed the butternut squash or pumpkin and cut it into small chunks. Slice the leek into small pieces add all squash and leek together with the thyme and kombu to a saucepan and cover with water. Bring it to the boil then simmer for approx 20 minutes until the squash is soft. Remove the kombu and thyme twigs and add the tofu cooking for five more minutes. Meanwhile dissolve the miso paste to half a cup of recently boiled water and add to the soup. Take off the heat and liquidize everything to a creamy consistency and serve adding salt or gomasio (sesame seed salt) to taste. Feel the muscles of your stomach relax as this creamy, savoury soup slides down.

Sweet Potato and Courgette Patties

These are fab and so easy. I could go on again about the health benefits of sweet potatoes and the slow release of energy roasting brings but you just have to make these, make tons of them and you will see why I recommend them. They keep really well in a Tupperware in the fridge and are great cold with chutney or a sweet and sour chilli sauce.

Makes about 8–10 patties

1 courgette, grated

1 sweet potato, grated

Large handful of chopped fresh coriander

100g Gram (chickpea) flour

Salt and pepper to taste

100mlwater

75ml sunflower oil

Mix the gram flour with the water, tablespoon by tablespoon until you have a thick batter, you may not have to add all the water. Stir the grated veg and coriander into the batter which will make it thinner. Heat the oil in a frying pan and drop large tablespoons of the mixture into the hot oil. Shallow fry for a couple of minutes and then turn over for another couple of minutes. The outside sticks should start to change colour, at this stage transfer to a lined oven tray and bake for 20–30 minutes. You can adapt this basic recipe by adding all sorts of vegetables, spices and herbs. My added extra favourites are feta cheese and scallions stirred into the batter.

Herby Millet

Use this recipe with the oven roasted vegetables to give your body comfort and your mind some rest. Millet is often referred to as the queen of grains, it has an extremely alkalizing effect on the stomach and is easily digested reducing danger of acid indigestion thereby allowing your body and mind to relax while digesting, increasing physical and mental recall ability.

25g butter
2 tablespoons sunflower oil
1 sliced onion
2 chopped cloves garlic
2 teaspoons finely chopped fresh parsley
100g millet
500 ml stock
1 tsp sage
¼ tsp thyme
Pinch of salt (depending on stock)

Heat butter and oil together in a heavy based saucepan add the onions and sauté them on a medium heat until they are translucent. Add the garlic and soften for a couple of minutes. Toss the millet and parsley into the saucepan so they absorb the juices, then add the stock, sage and thyme, bring to the boil and turn down to a gentle simmer for about 20 minutes. Ensure that the pan doesn't boil dry and add more stock if needed. I like my millet very wet, like soft stuffing, so I add plenty of stock. If you want a dry mix, like rice then for the last minute turn up the heat, keep stirring until the excess stock has evaporated.

Orange Cake

I know this recipe is cake and my intention is to provide naturally sweet alternatives to the big hitter of sugar but this recipe works in so many ways I couldn't leave it out. It is also my oldest recipe given to me by Judy Barack, my adopted mother when I was 19 and living on Kibbutz. It doesn't have the heady sticky sweetness of a regular cake as it uses olive oil instead of butter, because of this it also keeps brilliantly, getting better by the day if it's given the chance. I stand by the adage "a little of what you fancy does you good", so if you feel like cake, have one you've baked yourself with love and the spleen loves anything orange.

175g Self raising flour
150 g caster sugar
5 tbsp freshly squeezed orange juice
5 tbsp olive oil
2 eggs
1 tsp of vanilla extract
Zest of 1 orange

Mix flour and sugar into a bowl adding the orange juice, zest, vanilla extract, olive oil and egg yolks. Whisk the egg whites until they are stiff and fold them gently into the mixture. Grease an 18cm round spring form baking tin and pour in. Bake in a pre heated oven at 180 for about 40 minutes or until a squewer comes out clean.

Summer Cooler Tea

Mint has been used since Roman times as a healing herb. Its ability to soothe and relax involuntary muscles in the digestive tract means it helps with bloating and gas. However it can exacerbate acid reflux so just check in that is the tea for you. Rosehips are an extraordinarily rich source of vitamin C which improves blood circulation and regeneration of cells. My mother remembers being paid by the British Government to harvest Rosehips after World War II when citrus was in short supply. Mint and rosehip are great at reducing heat from the body especially in the stomach and the bladder.

2–3 tbsp of dried Rosehips
or 2–3 Rosehip teabags
1 ½ litres boiling water
Large handful of fresh mint

1 tbsp of honey or Apple Juice Concentrate
Calendula Petals

Place the rosehips and mint in a large jug or cafetiere and pour over the water. Give it a stir and let it brew for about five minutes. Add the honey, sprinkle over the calendula petals and roll on sunshine.

Specific Stomach/Spleen Points

Stomach 36 — The three mile point. ***Feel for the top of the tibia or shin bone on the outside. Fall diagonally off the bone and land in the hollow just below.*** This point is known as the three mile point as an ancient Chinese Emperor was able to march his army an extra three miles so whilst it is great at increasing stamina and energy be careful not to go past your own limits. Let it bring stability and grounding to your body and heal the effects of too much worrying and thinking.

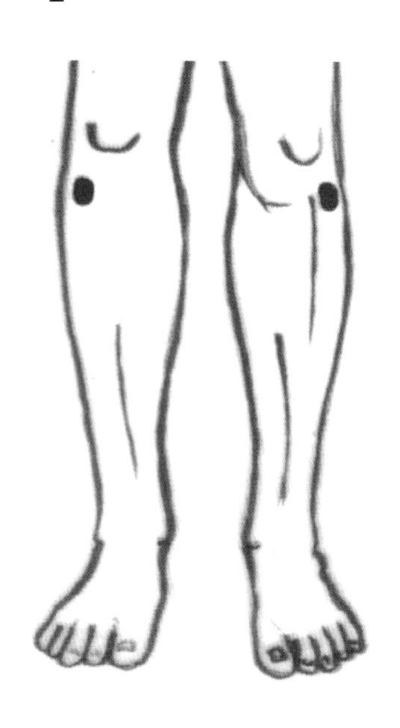

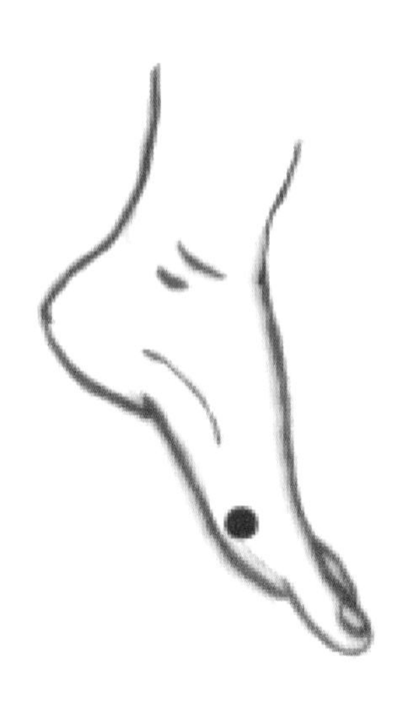

Spleen 3 — connection. ***On the inside of the foot where the pale and dark skin meet on the inside of the foot, feel for the depression at the back of the ball joint of the big toe. Stimulate this source point on the meridian to draw more chi from the source element of the earth.*** Physically it will help shift heaviness and dampness in the body, emotionally go and stand putting your feet on the earth and feel the support streaming up through this point into your body and you will receive receive, receive.

Specific Stomach/Spleen Points

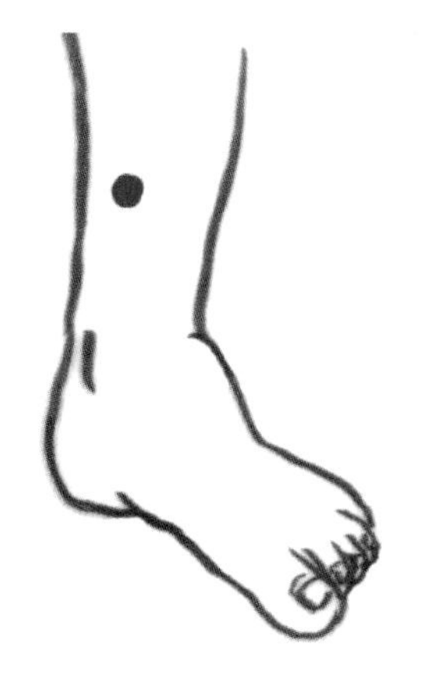

Spleen 6 — stimulating satisfaction. ***4 fingers up from the ankle bone on the inside mid line.*** This is a very strong point which releases tension in the abdomen and allows blood to flow evenly. It calms, relaxes and reduces irritability, so works well for menstrual or gynaecological problems but avoid during pregnancy.

Spleen 21 — the great embrace. ***Fold your arms across your chest and tuck your hands under your armpits. Where the little finger touches the ribs rub and press firmly for 30 seconds.*** This point relaxes the chest and allows energy to pass downwards from the shoulders and lungs binging a feeling of centred ease to the body. It will support it with energy if the joints are flabby whilst at the same time disperse the energy if there is pain. Press these points and accept what is you in this present moment. Be the centre of your own amazing, orbiting universe, ever changing, ever flowing, ever creating.

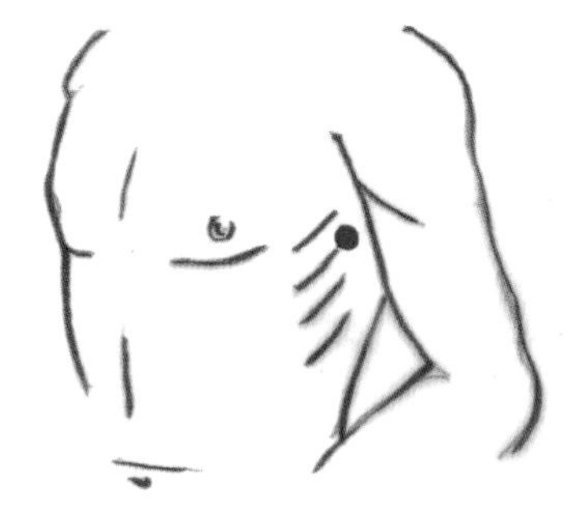

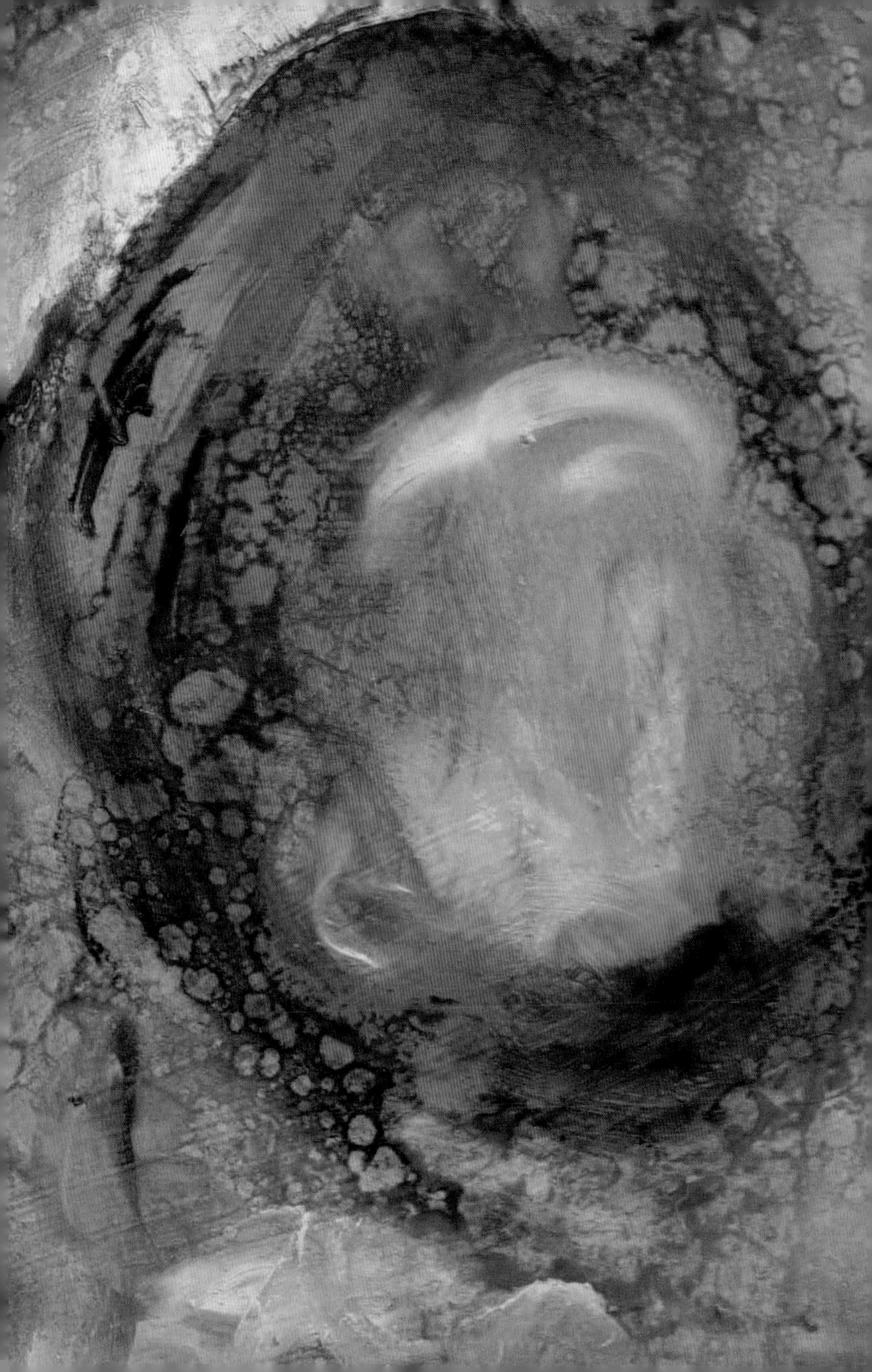

Where I am is where I am... Meant to be
When I relax, what I want,
is what comes to me.

Barefoot Doctor — Liberation

Motivation

Every action starts with a desire, conscious or unconscious; a reason as to why we are doing what we are doing. When I started to write this book here was/is mine:

"I want to make something beautiful. To put all the knowledge and information I have gained from all my teachers all my friends, my family, my adversaries and the wind into a simple beautiful book filled with love light and colour. In this way I am sharing and adding something positive to the collective field of expanding consciousness. This book says nothing new and really is there anything new to say, sometimes its good to remember what you know and bake a cake."

Acknowledgements

For wisdom, advice, reading the drafts, fixing the computer and in no order of importance *John Doherty, Sr Nuala Raleigh, Helen Sherry, Ken Hughes, Paula McHugh, Ali Welfare, Jasmine Itter, Rob Forde, Daire Shaw, Uta Kaiser, Liz Kavanagh, Abraham Hicks, Micheal, The Rain, Faith Amon, Sarah Chesworth, Eric Forsmark, Sinead O'Brien, David Mooney, Jennifer Crawford, Fatima Fernandez, Rose Conroy, Carmel Kelleher, Josephine Lynch, Anne Dreschler-Hyland, Sue Hardcastle, Cindy McMillan, Ciara Gogarty and my children Aaron, Zeph and Sam for being patient with a mother who wants to do too many things.*

Dedication

When my Nana was ill I sent her a letter to remind her of how wonderful she was. She gave us blankets chairs and a clothes horse to make tents in her back garden. She brought us tinned salmon sandwiches to eat in them and she stroked my hand in the quiet half hours while we stared at the fire. She gave me my first cup of tea and a love of Bovril on toast with soft boiled eggs. A couple of years later she died and they found the letter I had sent in her handbag. She had carried it with her. Everyone needs a letter like that to remind us of how truly wonderful we are.

So this book is dedicated to my mother. She sometimes finds it hard to hear how loveable she is so I am putting it here in a book to remind her. She taught me how to feed and care for a family. She taught me that with effort and love you could transform a few ingredients into nourishing, hearty food. Through the food I knew she loved me. No matter who I was, what I did or what she said there would always be a meal on the table for me. Sometimes my father's was on the wall but that's a different story. There is nothing so precious one human being can do for another than to provide that earthly support, so to my mother I am truly grateful.

Books I love & recommend

Recipes for Self Healing	Davrick Leggett
Healing with Wholefoods	Paul Pitchford
Like Water for Chocolate	Laura Esquval
Tibetan Book of Living & Dying	Sogyal Rinpoche
Nigella Express	Nigella Lawson
Plenty	Yotam Ottilenghi
The Food Doctor	Ian Marber & Vicki Edgson
Shiatsu Theory & Practice	Carola Beresford-Cooke

Joanne Faulkner

is a Shiatsu Practitioner. Through her practice in North County Dublin she specializes in the energy of food in Traditional Chinese Medicine to bring balance, healing and transformation for the body, mind and soul. Following the principles of Traditional Chinese Medicine she runs cookery classes, health retreats, and caters holistic events.

At 19 she travelled to Israel to live and work on a kibbutz. After working as a shepherdess and an avocado picker she ended up running the vegetable kitchen where she prepared vegetables and made salads for over 800 people every day. That was her introduction to cooking on a large scale. In 2002 she finished her three year Shiatsu training and it was integral that she link her love and knowledge of food to the powerful principles of Shiatsu and Traditional Chinese Medicine.

"Shiatsu enables me to attune to the body and see which meridians and organs are out of balance. The conscious cooking helps me to know what to do with the information the body gives me.

If we want to think clearly, sleep well and live a life full of joy we must take care of ourselves emotionally, mentally and physically. I love food, I love life."

wwww.joannefaulkner.org